CALIFORNIA INTEGRATED

Grade 7

elevate science

SAVVAS
LEARNING COMPANY

AUTHORS

You're an author!

As you write in this science book, your answers and personal discoveries will be recorded for you to keep, making this book unique to you. That is why you are one of the primary authors of this book.

✏️ **In the space below, print your name, school, town, and state. Then write a short autobiography that includes your interests and accomplishments.**

YOUR NAME ....

SCHOOL ....

TOWN, STATE ....

AUTOBIOGRAPHY ....

Your Photo

SAVVAS
LEARNING COMPANY

ISBN-13: 978-1-418-31038-7
ISBN-10:   1-418-31038-7
3   20

Program Authors

ZIPPORAH MILLER, Ed.D.
Coordinator for K-12 Science Programs, Anne Arundel County Public Schools
Dr. Zipporah Miller currently serves as the Senior Manager for Organizational Learning with the Anne Arundel County Public School System. Prior to that she served as the K-12 Coordinator for science in Anne Arundel County. She conducts national training to science stakeholders on the Next Generation Science Standards. Dr. Miller also served as the Associate Executive Director for Professional Development Programs and conferences at the National Science Teachers Association (NSTA) and served as a reviewer during the development of Next Generation Science Standards. Dr. Miller holds a doctoral degree from the University of Maryland College Park, a master's degree in school administration and supervision from Bowie State University and a bachelor's degree from Chadron State College.

MICHAEL J. PADILLA, Ph.D.
Professor Emeritus, Eugene P. Moore School of Education, Clemson University, Clemson, South Carolina
Michael J. Padilla taught science in middle and secondary schools, has more than 30 years of experience educating middle-school science teachers, and served as one of the writers of the 1996 U.S. National Science Education Standards. In recent years Mike has focused on teaching science to English Language Learners. His extensive experience as Principal Investigator on numerous National Science Foundation and U.S. Department of Education grants resulted in more than $35 million in funding to improve science education. He served as president of the National Science Teachers Association, the world's largest science teaching organization, in 2005–6.

MICHAEL E. WYSESSION, Ph.D
Professor of Earth and Planetary Sciences, Washington University, St. Louis, Missouri
Author of more than 100 science and science education publications, Dr. Wysession was awarded the prestigious National Science Foundation Presidential Faculty Fellowship and Packard Foundation Fellowship for his research in geophysics, primarily focused on using seismic tomography to determine the forces driving plate tectonics. Dr. Wysession is also a leader in geoscience literacy and education; he is the chair of the Earth Science Literacy Initiative, the author of several popular video lectures on geology in the *Great Courses* series, and a lead writer of the *Next Generation Science Standards**.

*Next Generation Science Standards is a registered trademark of Achieve. Neither Achieve nor the lead states and partners that developed the Next Generation Science Standards were involved in the production of this product, and do not endorse it. NGSS Lead States. 2013. *Next Generation Science Standards: For States, By States.* Washington, DC: The National Academies Press.

REVIEWERS

Program Consultants

Carol Baker
Science Curriculum

Dr. Carol K. Baker is superintendent for Lyons Elementary K-8 School District in Lyons, Illinois. Prior to this, she was Director of Curriculum for Science and Music in Oak Lawn, Illinois. Before this she taught Physics and Earth Science for 18 years. In the recent past, Dr. Baker also wrote assessment questions for ACT (EXPLORE and PLAN), was elected president of the Illinois Science Teachers Association from 2011–2013, and served as a member of the Museum of Science and Industry (Chicago) advisory board. She is a writer of the Next Generation Science Standards. Dr. Baker received her B.S. in Physics and a science teaching certification. She completed her master's of Educational Administration (K-12) and earned her doctorate in Educational Leadership.

Jim Cummins
ELL

Dr. Cummins's research focuses on literacy development in multilingual schools and the role technology plays in learning across the curriculum. *Elevate Science* incorporates research-based principles for integrating language with the teaching of academic content based on Dr. Cummins's work.

Elfrieda Hiebert
Literacy

Dr. Hiebert, a former primary-school teacher, is President and CEO of TextProject, a non-profit aimed at providing open-access resources for instruction of beginning and struggling readers, She is also a research associate at the University of California Santa Cruz. Her research addresses how fluency, vocabulary, and knowledge can be fostered through appropriate texts, and her contributions have been recognized through awards such as the Oscar Causey Award for Outstanding Contributions to Reading Research (Literacy Research Association, 2015), Research to Practice award (American Educational Research Association, 2013), and the William S. Gray Citation of Merit Award for Outstanding Contributions to Reading Research (International Reading Association, 2008).

Content Reviewers

Alex Blom, Ph.D.
Associate Professor
Department Of Physical Sciences
Alverno College
Milwaukee, Wisconsin

Joy Branlund, Ph.D.
Department of Physical Science
Southwestern Illinois College
Granite City, Illinois

Judy Calhoun
Associate Professor
Physical Sciences
Alverno College
Milwaukee, Wisconsin

Stefan Debbert
Associate Professor of Chemistry
Lawrence University
Appleton, Wisconsin

Diane Doser
Professor
Department of Geological Sciences
University of Texas at El Paso
El Paso, Texas

Rick Duhrkopf, Ph.D.
Department of Biology
Baylor University
Waco, Texas

Jennifer Liang
University of Minnesota Duluth
Duluth, Minnesota

Heather Mernitz, Ph.D.
Associate Professor of Physical
 Sciences
Alverno College
Milwaukee, Wisconsin

Joseph McCullough, Ph.D.
Cabrillo College
Aptos, California

Katie M. Nemeth, Ph.D.
Assistant Professor
College of Science and Engineering
University of Minnesota Duluth
Duluth, Minnesota

Maik Pertermann
Department of Geology
Western Wyoming Community College
Rock Springs, Wyoming

Scott Rochette
Department of the Earth Sciences
The College at Brockport
 State University of New York
Brockport, New York

David Schuster
Washington University in St Louis
St. Louis, Missouri

Shannon Stevenson
Department of Biology
University of Minnesota Duluth
Duluth, Minnesota

Paul Stoddard, Ph.D.
Department of Geology and
 Environmental Geosciences
Northern Illinois University
DeKalb, Illinois

Nancy Taylor
American Public University
Charles Town, West Virginia

Teacher Reviewers

Rita Armstrong
Los Cerritos Middle School
Thousand Oaks, California

Tyler C. Britt, Ed.S.
Curriculum & Instructional
Practice Coordinator
Raytown Quality Schools
Raytown, Missouri

Holly Bowser
Barstow High School
Barstow, California

David Budai
Coachella Valley Unified School District
Coachella, California

A. Colleen Campos
Grandview High School
Aurora, Colorado

Jodi DeRoos
Mojave River Academy
Colton, California

Colleen Duncan
Moore Middle School
Redlands, California

Nicole Hawke
Westside Elementary
Thermal, California

Margaret Henry
Lebanon Junior High School
Lebanon, Ohio

Ashley Humphrey
Riverside Preparatory Elementary
Oro Grande, California

Adrianne Kilzer
Riverside Preparatory Elementary
Oro Grande, California

Danielle King
Barstow Unified School District
Barstow, California

Kathryn Kooyman
Riverside Preparatory Elementary
Oro Grande, California

Esther Leonard M.Ed. and L.M.T.
Gifted and Talented Implementation Specialist
San Antonio Independent School District
San Antonio, Texas

Diana M. Maiorca, M.Ed.
Los Cerritos Middle School
Thousand Oaks, California

Kevin J. Maser, Ed.D.
H. Frank Carey Jr/Sr High School
Franklin Square, New York

Corey Mayle
Brogden Middle School
Durham, North Carolina

Keith McCarthy
George Washington Middle School
Wayne, New Jersey

Rudolph Patterson
Cobalt Institute of Math and Science
Victorville, California

Yolanda O. Peña
John F. Kennedy Junior High School
West Valley City, Utah

Stacey Phelps
Mojave River Academy
Oro Grande, California

Susan Pierce
Bryn Mawr Elementary
Redlands Unified School District
Redlands, California

Cristina Ramos
Mentone Elementary School
Redlands Unified School District
Mentone, California

Mary Regis
Franklin Elementary School
Redlands, California

Bryna Selig
Gaithersburg Middle School
Gaithersburg, Maryland

Pat (Patricia) Shane, Ph.D.
STEM & ELA Education Consultant
Chapel Hill, North Carolina

Elena Valencia
Coral Mountain Academy
Coachella, California

Janelle Vecchio
Mission Elementary School
Redlands, California

Brittney Wells
Riverside Preparatory Elementary
Oro Grande, California

Kristina Williams
Sequoia Middle School
Newbury Park, California

Safety Reviewers

Douglas Mandt, M.S.
Science Education Consultant
Edgewood, Washington

Juliana Textley, Ph.D.
Author, NSTA books on school science safety
Adjunct Professor
Lesley University
Cambridge, Massachusetts

California Spotlight
Instructional Segment 1

TOPIC 1

Introduction to Matter 8

Investigative Phenomenon How are models useful in describing how molecules are formed?

Quest PBL Lights! Camera! Action! 10

 MS-PS1-1, MS-PS1-2, EP&CIa, EP&CIIb, EP&CIVb

HANDS-ON LABS

▢ **Connect**
▢ **Investigate**
▢ **Demonstrate**

TOPIC 2 Solids, Liquids, and Gases 46

Investigative Phenomenon How can a model be used to describe what happens to particles when thermal energy is added or removed?

MS-PS1-4, EP&CIIb, EP&CIVb

HANDS-ON LABS
Connect
Investigate
Demonstrate

California Spotlight 🐻

Matter in Mono Lake

Elevate your thinking!

California Elevate Science takes science to a whole new level and lets you take ownership of your learning. Explore science in the world around you. Investigate how things work. Think critically and solve problems! *California Elevate Science* helps you think like a scientist, so you're ready for a world of discoveries.

Exploring California

California spotlights explore California phenomena. Topic Quests help connect lesson concepts together and reflect 3-dimensional learning.

- Science concepts organized around phenomena
- Topics weave together 3-D learning
- Engineering focused on solving problems and improving designs

California Spotlight
Instructional Segment 2

Before the Topics
Identify the Problem

California Flood Management

Phenomenon In February of 2017, workers at the Oroville Dam were forced to use the

Student Discourse

California Elevate Science promotes active discussion, higher order thinking and analysis and prepares you for high school through:

- High-level write-in prompts
- Evidence-based arguments
- Practice in speaking and writing

Model It

Crystalline and Amorphous Solids

Figure 5 ✏️ A pat of butter is an amorphous solid. The particles that make up the butter are not arranged in a regular pattern. The sapphire gem stones are crystalline solids. Draw what you think the particles look like in a crystalline solid.

☑ READING CHECK Explain In your own words, explain the main differences between crystalline solids and amorphous solids.

 **Quest** CHECK-IN

In this lesson, you learned what happens to the particles of substances during melting, freezing, evaporation, boiling, condensation, and sublimation. You also thought about how thermal energy plays a role in these changes of state.

Predict Why do you need to take the temperature of the surroundings into consideration when designing a system with materials that can change state?

Academic Vocabulary

In orange juice, bits of pulp are suspended in liquid. Explain what you think *suspended* means.

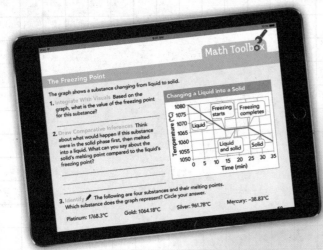

Build Literacy Skills

By connecting science to other disciplines like:

- Mathematics

- Reading and Writing

- STEM/Engineering

Focus on Inquiry

Case studies put you in the shoes of a scientist to solve real-world mysteries using real data. You will be able to:

- Analyze data

- Formulate claims

- Build evidence-based arguments

Enter the Digital Classroom

Virtual labs, 3-D expeditions, and dynamic videos take science beyond the classroom.

- Open-ended virtual labs

- Google Expeditions and field trips

- NBC Learn videos

What are the similarities and differences in matter between living and nonliving things?

Explore It

Look at the picture. What do you observe? What questions do you have about the phenomenon? Write your observations and questions in the space below.

....
....
....
....
....
....
....
....
....
....
....
....
....
....
....
....
....
....
....
....
....
....
....
....

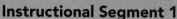
MS-PS1-1, MS-PS1-2, MS-PS1-4

Inquiry

- How does the matter in living and nonliving things differ?
- How does adding or removing thermal energy affect the physical states of matter?

Topics

1. Introduction to Matter
2. Solids, Liquids, and Gases

Before the Topics

Identify the Problem

Matter in Mono Lake

Phenomenon Mono Lake is located in the Great Basin of California, just east of Yosemite National Park. It is one of just a few saltwater lakes in the United States. The area around the lake is home to insects, birds, rabbits, mule deer, and mountain lions.

It may not seem like the living and nonliving things at Mono Lake have much in common other than sharing the same space. But they are made of the same types of atoms.

Mono Lake is home to a variety of organisms and unique geological structures.

The Chemistry of a Toad

One of the animals that makes its home in the area around Mono Lake is the Great Basin spadefoot toad. As its name implies, its habitat covers the Great Basin area, including the land around Mono Lake. The toad eats mostly insects, particularly ants. It spends much of its life buried in burrows that it digs, coming out only after it rains or at night to feed on insects. The toad requires sources of liquid water, such as seasonal ponds or lakes, to breed.

What matter makes up the toad? The six most common elements in living things are carbon, hydrogen, oxygen, nitrogen, phosphorus, and sulfur. The atoms of these elements combine to form thousands of different molecules. These molecules make up the different structures of the cells in the toad's body that carry out all the processes necessary for life.

Other elements are found in smaller amounts, but they play important roles. Sodium and potassium are necessary for the proper transmission of nerve impulses between the toad's brain and the rest of its body. Calcium, which is essential for bones, also allows the muscles in the toad's body to contract. This lets the toad move around in its environment.

If you look at the back foot of this toad, you can see the "spade" it uses to help dig its burrows.

Apply Concepts Describe how the Great Basin spadefoot toad interacts with matter in its environment.

....

....

....

The Chemistry of Mono Lake

Mono Lake is known for its rocky towers that rise up out of the water. It has several sources of water flowing into it but no water flowing out of it. If no water flows out, why doesn't the water in the lake become deeper over time? The climate in the Great Basin is hot and dry. As a result, the water in the lake evaporates as fast as new water enters the lake. As water evaporates, it leaves behind any salts the water sources carry into the lake. The water level might stay about the same, but the water itself contains large amounts of salts.

The material that makes up the towers is called tufa, which is a type of limestone. Limestone is made of calcium carbonate, a substance that contains calcium, carbon, and oxygen. Tufa towers form in carbonate-rich saltwater lakes (also known as soda lakes). In addition to the carbonate-rich water entering the lake, calcium-saturated water from mountain springs seeps into the lake. When the spring water meets the salty lake water, calcium and carbonate salts form calcium carbonate. This is the rock that makes up the tufa towers.

Depth of Mono Lake

Height (m) vs Year
- 1941: ~1,956
- 1982: ~1,943
- 2017: ~1,945

The graph shows that Mono Lake was much deeper years ago than it is now. The water reached its lowest observed level in 1982.

SEP Analyze Data Tufa forms only underwater. Use the graph to explain why these tufa towers emerge from the water.

....

....

....

Matter in Living and Nonliving Things

If living and nonliving things are made of the same atoms, then what accounts for the differences between them? How these atoms combine, the other atoms they combine with, and the number of atoms present are all factors that account for these differences. In this segment, you will learn more about matter and the atoms that make up all the matter around us.

When atoms of one element combine with atoms of another element, they can form different substances. These substances have different properties. For example, the toad and the tufa towers both contain carbon and calcium. But the natural processes that result in carbon and calcium combining to form the tufa towers do not occur in the toad.

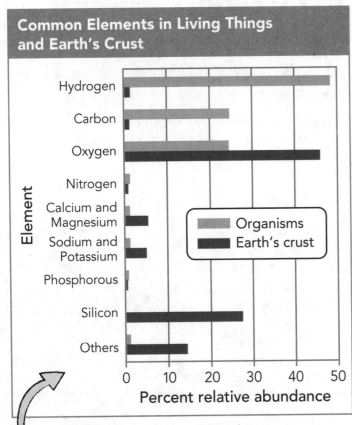

Common Elements in Living Things and Earth's Crust

Organisms
Earth's crust

Element: Hydrogen, Carbon, Oxygen, Nitrogen, Calcium and Magnesium, Sodium and Potassium, Phosphorous, Silicon, Others

Percent relative abundance: 0 10 20 30 40 50

This graph shows the percentage of common elements in living things, such as the Great Basin spadefoot toad, and in parts of Earth's crust, such as tufa towers. (Note that the data show abundance by number of atoms, not mass.)

1. **CCC Patterns** 🖊 Which two elements exist in approximately the same amounts in both organisms and Earth's crust? On the graph, circle the names of these elements.

2. **SEP Interpret Data** Water is made from hydrogen and oxygen. More than half of the body weight of most organisms—including humans—is made up of water. If the amount of hydrogen (H) and oxygen (O) shown on the graph reflects the amount of water an organism contains, how many atoms of hydrogen do you think combine with an atom of oxygen to form one molecule of water? Explain your answer.

....

....

....

....

....

....

....

Scientists Know What's the Matter

How do scientists determine the chemistry of different living and nonliving things? There are a variety of technologies that scientists use to test samples. These tools can provide information about things that we cannot directly observe. For example, an atom is too small to observe, even with a microscope. But it can be "weighed" with a special type of scale.

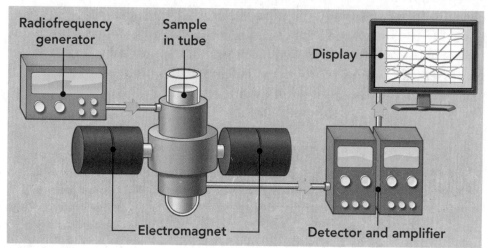

Nuclear Magnetic Resonance Spectroscopy Certain atoms act like tiny magnets, and they are arranged in a random pattern. This instrument causes atoms to line up in predictable patterns, allowing scientists to identify them.

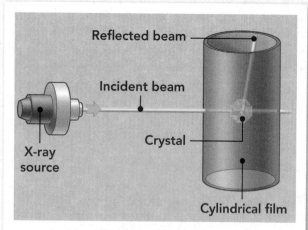

X-ray Diffractometer In solids, atoms are sometimes arranged in regular patterns, forming what is called a crystal. This instrument analyzes the pattern formed on the film when X-rays are deflected by atoms in the crystal.

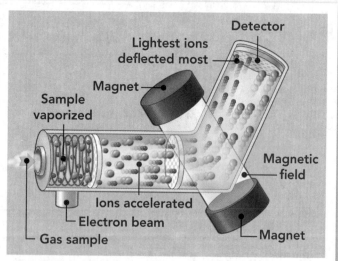

Mass Spectrometer Atoms are charged and then accelerated down a path. A magnet deflects the charged particles. Atoms can be identified according to how much they are deflected.

What questions can you ask to help you make sense of this phenomena?

Introduction to Matter

Investigative Phenomenon
How are models useful in describing how molecules are formed?

MS-PS1-1 Develop models to describe the atomic composition of simple molecules and extended structures.

MS-PS1-2 Analyze and interpret data on the properties of substances before and after the substances interact to determine if a chemical reaction has occurred.

EP&CIa Students should be developing an understanding that the goods produced by natural systems are essential to human life and to the functioning of our economies and cultures.

EP&CIIb Students should be developing an understanding that methods used to extract, harvest, transport, and consume natural resources influence the geographic extent, composition, biological diversity, and viability of natural systems.

EP&CIVb Students should be developing an understanding that the byproducts of human activity are not readily prevented from entering natural systems and may be beneficial, neutral, or detrimental in their effect.

What are this bird and this rock made of?

HANDS-ON LAB

μConnect See how you can model particles that are so small you can't see them.

What questions do you have about the phenomenon?

....

....

....

....

Quest PBL

How can you use science to make special effects?

Figure It Out A special effects company would like to be chosen to develop the special effects for a new movie. But first, the movie director wants to check out the company's capabilities. In this problem-based Quest activity, you will develop a movie scene that uses some amazing special effects. You will write the script and the storyboards. As you develop the special effects, you will explore different types of substances that are used to make special effects. You will understand the role that physical and chemical properties of matter play in the special effects. Finally, you will present your scene, along with an explanation of the special effects and the properties of matter behind them.

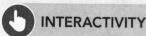 **INTERACTIVITY**

Lights! Camera! Action!

 MS-PS1-2

NBC LEARN ▶ VIDEO

After watching the Quest Kickoff video about special effects, complete the sentences about special effects you have seen in movies. Then discuss your answers with a partner.

1 One special effect I have seen is

....

....

....

2 It added to the scene because

....

....

....

Quest CHECK-IN

IN LESSON 1

How can substance changes play a role in special effects? Think about how you can take advantage of physical and chemical changes to create special effects.

 INTERACTIVITY

The Science of Special Effects

IN LESSON 2

How will the amounts of substances affect physical and chemical changes? Consider the amounts of substances you will need to create the special effects you want.

Quest CHECK-INS

IN LESSON 3

How do substances interact? Explore substances and how they interact. Collect and analyze data to help develop your special effects.

 INTERACTIVITY

Mysterious Movie Fog

HANDS-ON LAB

Cinematic Science

Hollywood is well known for its dazzling and dramatic special effects.

Quest FINDINGS

Complete the Quest!

Present your scene and storyboard, and include an explanation of the physical and chemical changes involved in your special effects.

👆 **INTERACTIVITY**

Reflect on Your Scene

① Describing and Classifying Matter

ʉInvestigate Develop your own models of atoms and molecules.

 MS-PS1-1 Develop models to describe the atomic composition of simple molecules and extended structure.

MS-PS1-2 Analyze and interpret data on the properties of substances before and after the substances interact to determine if a chemical reaction has occurred.

Connect It !

✏ **Several substances are shown in Figure 1. Two of the substances are in two different forms. Label these substances and each of their forms on the photo.**

SEP Analyze Data Is there any matter in **Figure 1** that you cannot see?

....

Form a Hypothesis What substance might affect the formation of volcanic rock?

....

Matter

Anything that has mass and takes up space is **matter**. Wood, metal, paper, glass, cloth, plastic, and air are all matter. In fact, you are made of matter, too. Scientists classify different types of matter by their properties. Some matter is visible, and some is not. Some types of matter are usually found in liquid form, and others are usually solid. Chemistry is the study of matter and how it changes.

One of the first steps in classifying matter is to determine whether something is a **substance**—a single kind of matter that always has a specific makeup, or composition. For example, sodium chloride is a substance known as table salt. It is considered a pure substance because its composition is the same whether you're looking at a single grain of salt or a boulder of salt taken from a salt mine. Sea salt, on the other hand, which is formed when seawater evaporates, is not a pure substance. There are many other substances in seawater, and those substances are left behind with sodium chloride when the water evaporates.

Matter on Earth
Figure 1 Hot lava cools in the Pacific Ocean to form this volcanic island.

Physical Properties

Whether you have a pure substance, such as gold, or a mixture, such as seawater, how it behaves and interacts with other substances depends on its properties. A **physical property** is a characteristic that can be observed without changing the matter into another type of matter. For example, gold melts at 1,064°C and boils at 2,856°C. It is an excellent conductor, meaning electricity moves through it very easily. Gold also has a high luster, or shininess, and a distinctive color. All of these characteristics are physical properties. They can be observed without changing the gold into something else. Two other physical properties are odor and solubility. Odor describes how substances smell. Vinegar, for example, has a very distinct odor that is easy to recognize.

Solubility describes how easily a substance dissolves in another substance, such as water. Vinegar is very soluble, meaning it easily dissolves in water. These properties, like boiling point, are easily observed without changing the identity of vinegar.

Physical and Chemical Properties

Figure 2 Can you tell physical and chemical properties apart?

1. **SEP Evaluate Information** Analyze the photos and read their captions. Write "physical" or "chemical" next to "Property".

2. **SEP Engage in Argument** Below each photo, cite evidence that guided you to classify the properties as physical or chemical.

Water and carbon dioxide in the leaves of the coconut palm tree are converted to oxygen and sugar, thanks to the energy provided by the sun.

Oxygen is a substance that dissolves in water. Fish absorb oxygen from the water. When dissolved oxygen levels are low, it can be hard for organisms to survive.

Property

Evidence

....

....

....

Property

Evidence

....

....

....

Chemical Properties Other properties can only be observed by combining or breaking apart substances. These are **chemical properties**—characteristics that describe the ability of a substance to become something else. For example, if you inject carbon dioxide gas into liquid water, some of the water will react with the carbon dioxide to produce carbonic acid. This ability to react is a chemical property of water. Likewise, the ability of carbon dioxide to combine with water and become carbonic acid is a chemical property. Another example of a chemical property is flammability. Flammability is a measure of how easily something burns.

Look at the images in **Figure 2** and read their captions. The images and captions will help you determine whether chemical or physical properties are being described.

✓ CHECK POINT **Apply Concepts** Methane is a highly flammable substance. When it combines with oxygen, it burns and produces carbon dioxide. Use this example to explain why flammability is a chemical property and not a physical property.

....

....

Literacy Connection

Integrate with Visuals As you determine whether the images and descriptions involve physical or chemical properties, set up a two-column table in your notebook in which you can record and classify examples of physical and chemical properties.

Reflect Think of the changes shown on these pages. Which can be reversed, and which cannot? Why is reversibility not a reliable way to distinguish physical and chemical changes?

If iron is exposed to air and water, it can rust.

Property

Evidence

....

....

....

Wood tends to be hard and relatively inflexible, especially when it's been dried. This is why wood is an excellent building material.

Property

Evidence

....

....

....

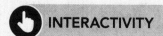
Components of Matter

There are many particles you can see, such as grains of sand. Have you ever wondered whether these tiny grains have even smaller particles inside? They do! The particle theory of matter explains that all matter is made up of very tiny particles called atoms.

Atoms An **atom** is the basic unit from which all matter is made. Different substances are made up of different types of atoms. But all atoms have the same basic structure.

Elements Substances that are made up of only one type of atom are called **elements**. For instance, the element aluminum is made of only aluminum atoms, and no other pure substance has atoms like aluminum's atoms. Each element can be identified by its specific physical and chemical properties. You may already be familiar with some elements such as gold, oxygen, and carbon (**Figure 3**). These cannot be broken down into different substances. Elements are represented by one- or two-letter symbols, such as O for oxygen and Al for aluminum.

Atoms Combining

Figure 3 Diamond and graphite are extended structures of the same element: carbon. Diamond, the hardest natural substance, forms under intense pressure, with atoms packed tightly together. Carbon atoms form layers in graphite, which easily slide and break off.

The structures represented by the ball and stick models are far too small to see.

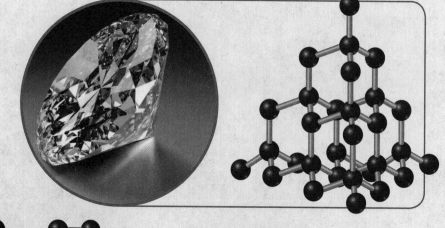

Molecules Most atoms can combine with other atoms. When this happens, a chemical bond forms. A chemical bond is a force of attraction between two or more atoms. Sometimes, atoms combine to form extended structures. One type of extended structure is a molecule. A **molecule** is a group of two or more atoms held together by chemical bonds. A molecule of carbon dioxide, as shown in **Figure 4** for example, is made up of a carbon atom chemically bonded to two oxygen atoms. Two atoms of the same element can also combine to form a molecule. For example, a hydrogen molecule is made up of two hydrogen atoms. Some large molecules are made of thousands of atoms!

HANDS-ON LAB

☑Investigate Develop your own models of atoms and molecules.

Model It!

Molecules and Atoms

Figure 4 Explain Phenomena The four molecules shown here are made of different combinations of carbon, oxygen, or hydrogen atoms. Below each molecule, list the types of atoms in it and how many atoms there are of each type. The first answer is completed as an example.

Water	Oxygen	Carbon dioxide	Methane

1 oxygen atom,
....
2 hydrogen atoms
....

SEP Develop Models ✏
Draw a model of a two-atom molecule of hydrogen and label the atoms.

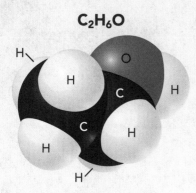

C₂H₆O

Compound From Corn

Figure 5 Ethanol is a chemical compound made from sugars in corn and other plants. It can be burned to power engines.

👆 **INTERACTIVITY**

Develop models of extended structures including molecules.

Compounds When a molecule contains more than one element, it is called a compound. A **compound** is a substance made of two or more elements that are chemically combined in a set ratio. A compound is represented by a chemical formula, which shows the elements in the compound and the ratio of atoms. For example, the chemical formula for carbon dioxide is CO_2. The subscript *2* tells you that every molecule of carbon dioxide contains two oxygen atoms. If there is no number after an element's symbol, it is understood that the number is 1. In CO_2, there is one carbon atom. The ratio of carbon to oxygen is 1 to 2.

When elements chemically combine, they form compounds with properties different from those of the individual elements. Ethanol, shown in **Figure 5**, is a compound that contains carbon, but because it also contains hydrogen and oxygen, and the molecule has a particular shape, it has different properties than the pure forms of carbon, hydrogen, and oxygen. There are many different compounds made of different combinations and configurations of those three elements.

☑ CHECK POINT **Integrate with Visuals** How are pure carbon, oxygen, and hydrogen different from the compound ethanol, which contains all three of those elements?

....

....

....

....

Types of Mixtures

You have learned that elements and compounds are substances. Most of the things found in nature, however, are not simple elements or compounds—they are mixtures. A **mixture** is made up of two or more substances that are together in the same place, but their atoms are not chemically bonded.

Mixtures differ from compounds. Each substance in a mixture keeps its own properties. Also, the parts of a mixture are not necessarily combined in a set ratio. Look at **Figure 6A**, which shows a bowl of mixed nuts. They are mixed together, but they are not chemically bonded to each other. This type of mixture is known as a heterogeneous mixture.

A homogeneous mixture is different from a heterogeneous mixture. In a homogeneous mixture, it is difficult or impossible to see the different parts. Combining dry ingredients for baking results in a homogeneous mixture, as shown in **Figure 6B**. Air is another homogeneous mixture, made of gases rather than solids. You know that oxygen is present in the air because you are able to breathe, but you cannot pinpoint exactly where the oxygen is in the air. A solution is a liquid example of a homogeneous mixture. Salt water is an example of a solution.

If you want to separate a mixture, you need to divide its parts according to their properties. This is possible because the substances in a mixture retain their own properties. The methods you can use to separate the parts of a mixture include distillation, evaporation, filtration, and magnetic attraction.

Magnetic attraction involves holding a magnet near a mixture to pull out anything that is attracted to the magnet, such as a metal. Evaporation is a good way to separate dissolved or suspended substances from water. This is how sea salt is harvested from the ocean. In filtration, a substance is passed through some kind of filter that allows fine particles, such as molecules of water, to pass through while filtering out larger particles. **Distillation** involves separating liquids by boiling them. The liquid with the lower boiling point will vaporize first, leaving the other liquid behind.

✓ CHECK POINT Apply Scientific Reasoning Think about a lake. Would you describe it as a homogeneous mixture, heterogeneous mixture, or both? Explain.

....

....

....

Heterogeneous and Homogeneous Mixtures

Figure 6 A bowl of mixed nuts is a heterogeneous mixture. A bowl of cake mix is a homogeneous mixture.

 VIDEO

Learn more about physical and chemical properties.

Academic Vocabulary

Someone may ask you to distill a complicated idea into a brief summary that gets right to the point. How does this relate to distillation in chemistry?

....

....

....

....

☑ LESSON 1 Check

Ammonia

Key

Hydrogen

Nitrogen

1. Identify What is the chemical formula for the molecule shown?

....

....

....

2. SEP Evaluate Information Suppose you find a website that describes the rusting of a nail as a change to only the physical properties of iron. Would that be accurate? Explain.

....

....

....

....

....

....

3. SEP Construct Explanations What is the difference between a molecule and a compound?

....

....

....

....

....

....

....

....

....

....

....

....

....

....

Quest CHECK-IN

In this lesson, you learned about the properties that are used to describe matter. You also learned about mixtures and how they are classified as well as how their components can be separated.

SEP Define Problems Why is it important to know what substances you have available to work with, and how they might change, when developing special effects?

....

....

....

....

INTERACTIVITY

The Science of Special Effects

Go online to learn about how different substances can be combined in various ways to achieve different outcomes.

CAREERS
Museum Technician

Saving the World's Art

The world is full of works of art, from the delicate to the majestic, from the ancient to the new. Many are made of organic materials, such as paint, canvas, and wood. Others are made of ceramics or stone. These materials are sensitive to changes in temperature and humidity. They break down as they age, just as living creatures do. This is where the museum technicians come in! It's their job to restore works of art.

If you are strongly interested in both science and art, a career as a museum technician might be perfect for you! It combines an appreciation of art, architecture, and sculpture with a detailed knowledge of the chemistry that breaks down artwork. Understanding chemistry helps to restore art to its original beauty.

▶ **VIDEO**

Learn how a museum technician restores pieces of art.

MY CAREER

Type "museum technician" into an online search engine to learn more about this career.

Before

After

This is a painting on the ceiling on the Sistine Chapel after restoration. The inset shows what it looked like before.

② Measuring Matter

HANDS-ON LAB

⚗️Investigate Explore the physical properties of mass, volume, and density.

MS-PS1-2 Analyze and interpret data on the properties of substances before and after the substances interact to determine if a chemical reaction has occurred.

Connect It !

✎ **In the fruit market photo, outline three things that have mass.**

Hypothesize How much do you think an apple weighs?

....

CCC Scale, Proportion, and Quantity How do you think an object's mass relates to its weight?

....

....

....

Expressing Weight, Mass, and Volume

Recall that matter is anything that has mass and takes up space. **Mass** is the amount of matter in an object. An object's mass does not change even if the force of gravity upon the object changes. The amount of space that matter occupies is called its **volume**. All forms of matter—solids, liquids, and gases—have volume. If you want to measure matter, such as the fruit in **Figure 1**, you need to measure both mass and volume.

Weight First, consider weight. **Weight** is a measure of the force of gravity on an object. The force of gravity depends on the mass of the planet or moon where the object is being weighed. Because the moon has much less mass than Earth, on the moon you would weigh about one sixth of what you weigh on Earth. Jupiter has much more mass than Earth. On Jupiter, you would weigh more than twice what you weigh on Earth.

To find the weight of an object, you could place it on a scale like the ones shown in **Figure 2**. The object's weight pulls down on a mechanism inside the scale. The mechanism is calibrated in such a way that the object's weight is displayed on the face of the scale.

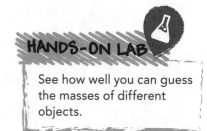

HANDS-ON LAB

See how well you can guess the masses of different objects.

Fruit Matter
Figure 1 At a farmer's market, you can buy fruit by the pound. A pound is a unit of weight.

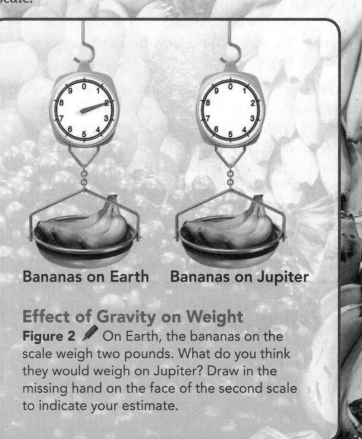

Bananas on Earth   **Bananas on Jupiter**

Effect of Gravity on Weight
Figure 2 🖊 On Earth, the bananas on the scale weigh two pounds. What do you think they would weigh on Jupiter? Draw in the missing hand on the face of the second scale to indicate your estimate.

Triple-Beam Balance Scale

Figure 3 A mechanical scale is like a seesaw. An object of unknown mass is put on one side of the scale, and then weighted tabs are moved on the other side of the fulcrum until the two sides are in balance. Gravity is acting on both sides with the same force, so it is not a factor in measuring mass this way.

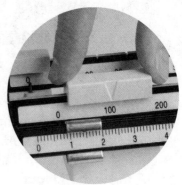

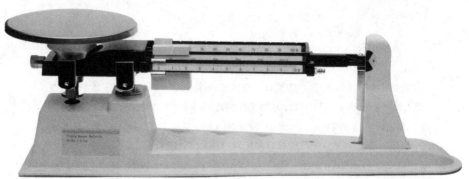

Literacy Connection

Cite Textual Evidence
Underline the text that explains why you cannot rely on measurements of weight to measure mass.

Academic Vocabulary

In this context, how is the term *convert* different from the term *change*? Can you think of another example that captures the difference?

....

....

....

....

....

....

....

....

....

Mass Weight changes as the force of gravity changes. Even between different places on Earth, the force of gravity has slight variation, so your weight would vary as well. This means there should be a measure of matter that is not affected by gravity. That's where mass comes in. Remember that mass does not change with location even if the force of gravity changes. For this reason, scientists prefer to describe matter in terms of mass rather than weight.

Scales that measure mass are designed to compare the known mass of an object to the unknown mass of another object (**Figure 3**). To measure mass, scientists use a system called the International System of Units (SI). The SI unit of mass is the kilogram (kg). People in the United States use pounds to measure weight. You can **convert** pounds to kilograms when the force of gravity at a location is known. If you weigh 130 pounds on Earth, your mass is about 60 kilograms, because a kilogram is equivalent to about 2.2 pounds. Sometimes, a smaller unit known as a gram (g) is used to measure mass. There are 1,000 grams in a kilogram, or 0.001 kilogram in a gram.

☑ **CHECK POINT** **Summarize** What are weight, mass, and volume?

....

....

....

Volume Volume is the amount of space that matter takes up. Scientists generally measure the volume of solids in the SI units of cubic meters (m³), cubic centimeters (cm³), or cubic millimeters (mm³). They measure the volume of liquids in liters (L) and milliliters (mL). A milliliter is 1/1,000 of a liter and has the same volume as 1 cubic centimeter. Gases do not have a definite volume because their particles move to fill their containers. So the volume of a gas is measured in the units of its container.

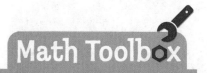

Math Toolbox

Calculating Volume

Objects of Regular Shape

The volume of an object of regular shape can be calculated by measuring the object's dimensions. At California's LAX airport, the volume of a boxlike piece of carry-on luggage that is 20 cm deep, 30 cm wide, and 45 cm long can be calculated by using this formula:

Volume = Length × Width × Height

1. SEP Use Mathematics What is the volume of the bag?

....

2. SEP Use Mathematics Large numbers can be rewritten by multiplying a number times a power of ten. For example, because 10^4 is equal to 10,000, you can rewrite 30,000 as 3×10^4. Rewrite your answer to Question 1 in this form.

....

Objects of Irregular Shape

One way to find the volume of an irregularly shaped object is by submerging it in a volume of water that is known. The volume of water that is displaced equals the volume of the object.

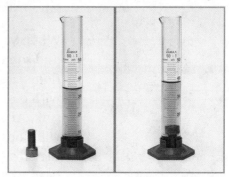

3. SEP Design Solutions Suppose the irregularly shaped object is a leopard shark, like the one here at the Monterey Bay Aquarium in California. It is about to be moved into a cube-shaped aquarium tank. How might you combine the "Length × Width × Height" formula with the displacement method to determine the shark's volume? Explain.

....

....

....

....

....

....

Determining Density

A kilogram of sand takes up much less space than a kilogram of feathers. The volumes differ because sand and feathers have different densities—another important property of matter. **Density** is a measure of the mass of a material in a given volume.

Calculating Density Density is a ratio of mass to volume. It can be expressed as the number of grams in one cubic centimeter (g/cm^3). For example, the density of water at room temperature is stated as "one gram per cubic centimeter" ($1\ g/cm^3$). Recall that volume can also be measured in milliliters. So the density of water can also be expressed as $1\ g/mL$. You can determine the density of a sample of matter by dividing its mass by its volume.

$$\text{Density} = \frac{\text{Mass}}{\text{Volume}}$$

When you drop things into bodies of water, some things sink and some things float. What determines whether something floats? You know the density of fresh water is $1\ g/cm^3$. An object with a density greater than that of water, such as a rock, will sink. An object with a lesser density, such as a piece of wood, will float. If you shake a bottle of oil and vinegar, you will see the oil slowly separate to float above the vinegar. This happens because oil is less dense than vinegar.

Density and Water

Figure 4 This boy is skipping stones at Point Lobos State Reserve in Monterey County, California. Why do the stones sink to the bottom of the water?

....

....

....

Model It

Liquid Layers
This beaker shows five layers of liquids of various densities. The liquids are listed in the table below.

Liquid	Density
vegetable oil	0.91 g/mL
honey	1.36 g/mL
corn syrup	1.33 g/mL
water	1.00 g/mL
dish soap	1.03 g/mL

SEP Develop Models ✏ Complete the model by using different shading for each layer shown, according to the densities in the table. Then, label each of the substances.

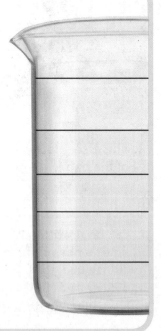

Density and Temperature You know that mass is a physical property. Density is a function of mass and volume, so it too is a physical property. Note that increasing or decreasing the total amount of a given substance won't change its density. Suppose you have two bars of silver, one 5 cubic centimeters and the other 75 cubic centimeters. They will both have the same density because they are both made of the same substance.

One factor that does affect density is temperature. In general, most substances become less dense as temperature increases and more dense as temperature decreases. This is why warm masses of air rise up from Earth's surface and cold air masses sink toward Earth's surface. Water also follows this general rule, but not always. Liquid water does expand, or get less dense, when it gets warmer. It condenses, or gets denser, as it gets colder. But when water cools below 4°C, its density actually begins to decrease again, as you can see in the Math Toolbox.

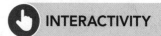

INTERACTIVITY

Investigate density using various materials including solid and liquid water.

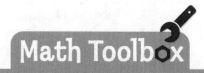

HANDS-ON LAB

ⁱⁿInvestigate Explore the physical properties of mass, volume, and density.

Math Toolbox

Temperature and Density of Water

Although the density of water is usually considered to be 1 g/cm³, the true density of water varies with temperature, as shown in the table and graph.

1. **Claim** At what temperature is water densest? Circle that point on the graph and record your answer here.

....

2. **Evidence** Explain the sudden decrease in density when water is at 0°C as shown on the graph.

....

....

....

3. **Reasoning** If ice were, like most other substances, more dense than its liquid form, what would this mean for bodies of water that freeze in the winter? What would happen to the organisms that live in them?

....

....

....

....

....

Density of Water vs. Temperature

Temperature (°C)	Density (g/cm³)
0 (ice)	0.9168
0 (water)	0.9998
4	1.0000
10	0.9997
25	0.9977

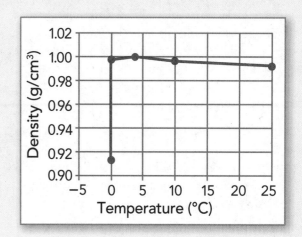

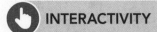

INTERACTIVITY

Compare the weights, masses, and densities of objects on Earth versus on the moon.

VIDEO

See what your weight and mass would be on Mars.

Using Density

Because density is an intrinsic property of matter, meaning that it does not change with the shape of an object, density can be used to identify substances. Imagine that you are looking for gold in streambeds in California. You find an area where the gravelly streambed seems to be flecked with gold. First, you sort the gold-colored pieces from the other parts of the sediment. You set aside four of the largest pieces, hoping at least one of them will be valuable gold. You use a small digital scale and a graduated cylinder filled with water to measure the masses and volumes of each sample. Those data are shown below each sample in the Math Toolbox. If one of the samples has a density of 19.3 g/cm^3, then you've found gold!

Math Toolbox

Densities of Unknown Substances

5.0 g/cm^3

19.3 g/cm^3

2.8 g/cm^3

3.0 g/cm^3

	Gold	Muscovite	Biotite	Pyrite
Mass	284 g	67.2 g	60 g	120 g
Volume	14.7 cm^3	24 cm^3	20 cm^3	24 cm^3
Density				

These four minerals are all mined in California. Although they look similar, they all have different densities. This physical property can help you determine which is really gold.

1. **SEP Use Mathematics** ✏ Find the ratio of the mass and volume measurements given for each substance to calculate the density of each sample. Record your calculations in the table.

2. **Identify** ✏ Based on the densities you've calculated, write the correct names of the substances in the labels by the minerals.

3. **SEP Design Solutions** Besides density, what other physical property can you use to confirm that the gold is indeed real gold? Describe how you would conduct a test to confirm the sample's identity.

....

....

....

....

....

....

☑ LESSON 2 Check

1. **SEP Use Mathematics** What is the mass of a sample of a substance with a volume of 120 mL and a density of 0.75 g/mL?

   ....

2. **Explain** If density usually increases with decreasing temperature, why does ice float on liquid water?

   ....

   ....

   ....

3. **SEP Engage in Argument** Why is mass a better unit for measuring matter than weight?

   ....

   ....

   ....

4. **SEP Use Mathematics** ✏ The force of gravity on the moon is only 16.6% the force of gravity on Earth. For each item listed in the table below, fill in what its weight would be on the moon.

Weights on Earth and the Moon		
Item	Weight on Earth	Weight on the Moon
Apple	150 g	
Hammer	1.5 lb	
Person	180 lb	
Blue whale	200 tons	

5. **SEP Use Mathematics** A small bar of pure gold with a density 19.3 g/cm³ displaces 80 cm³ of water when dropped into a beaker. What is the mass of the bar of gold?

   ....

6. **CCC Cause and Effect** What might happen if a large cloud in the sky suddenly encountered a colder air mass with a temperature of 5°C?

   ....

   ....

   ....

   ....

7. **SEP Engage in Argument** In much of the world, SI units are used in everyday life and not just in science. Why would it make sense for people in the United States to use SI units in everyday life, too? Explain using math terms such as *calculate* and *convert*.

   ....

   ....

   ....

   ....

   ....

   ....

   ....

   ....

   ....

   ....

   ....

(3) Changes in Matter

HANDS-ON LAB

иInvestigate Explore physical and chemical changes.

MS-PS1-2 Analyze and interpret data on the properties of substances before and after the substances interact to determine if a chemical reaction has occurred.

Connect It!

✏️ **Circle part of a tree that is undergoing the process of changing matter.**

CCC Stability and Change What causes the material that makes up the tree to change its state of matter?

....

Form a Hypothesis Why do you think matter changes state when outside forces act upon it?

....

....

....

Physical Changes in Matter

A **physical change** alters the form or appearance of matter but does not turn any substance in the matter into a different substance. If you accidentally drop a glass onto a hard floor, the glass may shatter. However, the chemical composition of the broken glass is still the same. A substance that undergoes a physical change is still the same substance after the change.

Changes of State You have learned that most matter exists in three different states—solids, liquids, and gases. Suppose you leave an ice cube in a glass and forget about it. When you come back, there is a small amount of water in the glass. The ice cube has undergone a physical change. The solid water that made up the ice cube has melted into liquid water. A change in state, such as from a solid to a liquid or from a liquid to a gas, is an example of a physical change.

HANDS-ON LAB

Use chalk to distinguish between physical and chemical changes.

Reflect As you read this lesson, record examples of physical and chemical changes that you encounter, as well as examples that you think of from your own life. How does the difference between chemical and physical changes make the phenomena easier to understand?

Changing States
Figure 1 Wildfires, such as the 2016 Sand Fire in southern California shown here, can cause changes in states of matter.

Changes in Shape or Form

When you combine two substances, how do you know if just a physical change occurred or whether you have created an altogether new substance? There are ways to figure it out. For example, imagine that you pour a teaspoon of sugar into a glass of water and stir until the sugar dissolves. If you pour the sugar solution into a pan and boil away the water, the sugar will remain as a crust at the bottom of the pan. The crust may not look exactly like the sugar before you dissolved it, but it's still sugar. Therefore, dissolving is a physical change.

Other examples of physical changes include bending, crushing, breaking, and carving (**Figure 2**). Any change that alters only the shape or form of matter is a physical change. Methods of separating mixtures, such as filtration and distillation, also involve physical changes.

✔CHECK POINT **Explain** How are melting and carving ice sculptures both examples of physical changes?

....
....
....
....

Sculpting Ice

Figure 2 An ice scultpor breaks ice and shapes ice, but he or she does not cause it to change into another substance.

Model It !

Types of Physical Changes

🖊 Make a paper airplane out of a piece of scrap paper. Draw a sketch of your paper airplane in the space provided.

1. **CCC Cause and Effect** What kinds of physical changes did you cause to happen to the paper?

....
....

2. **CCC Stability and Change** How can paper that has already been used be physically changed to make other paper products?

....
....
....
....

Chemical Changes in Matter

A change in matter that produces one or more new substances is a **chemical change**, or chemical reaction. In some chemical changes, a single substance breaks down into two or more other substances. For example, hydrogen peroxide breaks down into water and oxygen gas when it's poured on a cut on your skin. In other chemical changes, two or more substances combine to form different substances. Photosynthesis is a natural chemical change that occurs in plants and other photosynthetic organisms. Several compounds are combined using energy from the sun to produce new substances.

Some chemical changes can be initiated and observed in the kitchen. If you have ever baked bread with help from yeast, you have seen a chemical reaction at work. The yeast reacts with sugars in the mixture to produce bubbles of carbon dioxide, which make the dough rise (**Figure 3A**). Another chemical reaction takes place on the surface of the bread. As heat is added, the sugars turn into a brown crust (**Figure 3B**). As in many chemical reactions, changes in properties show that new substances have formed.

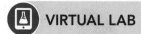

VIRTUAL LAB

Complete a virtual lab about chocolate.

Chemical Change in the Kitchen

Figure 3 Adding yeast to dough causes a chemical change, which makes the dough rise.

 A

Adding heat to the dough causes sugars to undergo a chemical change that results in a brown crust.

 B

Tarnishing is the slow combination of a bright metal, such as silver, with sulfur or another substance, which produces a dark coating on the metal.

Oxidation is the combination of a substance with oxygen, as happens when iron rusts.

Objects catch fire when a fuel combines rapidly with oxygen, producing heat, light, and new substances.

Bubbles are created by using electricity to break a compound down into elements or simpler compounds.

Types of Chemical Change

Figure 4 The images show different types of chemical changes. Next to each photo, identify the changes in properties and other evidence that a new substance has formed.

Examples of Chemical Change One common chemical change is the burning of natural gas on a gas stove. Natural gas is mostly made up of the compound methane (CH_4). When it burns, methane combines with oxygen in the air and forms new substances. The new substances include carbon dioxide gas (CO_2) and water vapor (H_2O). Both of these substances can be identified from their properties, which are different from those of methane. **Figure 4** describes some of the types of chemical changes.

Conservation of Mass When something such as a piece of paper burns, it may seem to lose mass or disappear. Scientists, however, have proved that it does not. In the 1770s, the French chemist Antoine Lavoisier measured mass both before and after a chemical change. His data showed that no mass was lost or gained during the change. The fact that matter is not created or destroyed in any chemical or physical change is called the law of **conservation** of mass. This law is also called the law of conservation of matter, because mass is a measurement of matter.

Student Discourse
Where else have you heard the term *conservation*? With a partner, discuss how the term's meaning in that other context relates to its meaning in chemistry. Record your ideas in your notebook.

CHECK POINT **Infer** Why do you think the conservation of mass pertains more to chemical changes than physical changes?

....

....

....

....

HANDS-ON LAB

Investigate Explore physical and chemical changes.

Math Toolbox

Conservation of Mass

The combustion reaction that produces carbon dioxide and water from methane and oxygen does not result in any gain or loss of mass. All atoms that go into the reaction are present at the end of the reaction. Even though the types of atoms do not change, it is evident that a chemical reaction has occurred because the properties of the carbon dioxide and water are different than the properties of the methane and oxygen.

| Methane molecule | Two oxygen molecules | | Carbon dioxide molecule | Two water molecules |

| ☐ Carbon atom(s) | ☐ Hydrogen atom(s) | ☐ Oxygen atom(s) | | ☐ Carbon atom(s) | ☐ Hydrogen atom(s) | ☐ Oxygen atom(s) |

1. **SEP Use Models** ✎ Count the atoms of each element before and after the chemical change. Fill in the numbers in the appropriate boxes.

2. **Use Ratio Reasoning** Does the ratio of hydrogen to oxygen change during the reaction? How do you know?

....

....

3. **SEP Ask Questions** Antoine Lavoisier was able to show that mass wasn't lost or gained during chemical reactions by weighing all of the matter in the system before and after reactions occurred. What questions would you ask Lavoisier about how he conducted his investigations?

....

....

Energy and Matter Are Related

Do you have much energy for schoolwork today? In science, energy is the ability to do work or cause change. Any kind of change to matter involves a change in energy. Bending a paper clip or chopping an onion takes energy. When ice changes to liquid water, energy is absorbed from the matter around it.

Like matter, energy is conserved in a chemical change. Energy is never created or destroyed. It is only transformed.

Temperature and Thermal Energy When you walk into a warm building on a cold winter day, you will immediately notice the difference between the cold outside and the warmth inside. We refer to the measure of how hot or cold something is as temperature. Temperature is related to the motion and energy of the particles of matter. The particles of gas in the cold outside air have less average energy of motion than the particles of air inside the warm building.

The total energy of the motion of all of the particles in an object is known as thermal energy. People often talk about thermal energy in terms of how hot or cold something is, but thermal energy is not the same thing as temperature. Thermal energy naturally flows from warmer matter to cooler matter.

Literacy Connection

Write Explanatory Texts How can you use terms such as *thermal energy*, *particles*, *motion*, and *flow* to explain the movement of heat in our world?

....

....

....

....

....

Movement of Thermal Energy

Figure 5 ✏ A polar bear swims in frigid waters of the Arctic, while people relax in a warm geothermal pool in Iceland. Draw arrows to indicate the direction that thermal energy moves in each image.

Thermal Energy and Changes in Matter

When matter changes, thermal energy is usually released or absorbed. For example, ice absorbs thermal energy from its surroundings when it melts, leaving the air around it feeling cold. That's why coolers for food and drinks are filled with ice. The melting of ice is a change in which energy is absorbed. Combustion is an example of a change in which energy is released.

Chemical energy is stored in the chemical bonds between atoms. Foods, fuels, and even the cells in your body store chemical energy. Burning fuels transforms chemical energy and releases some of it as thermal energy. When you ride a bike up a hill, chemical energy from food changes into the energy of your muscles' motion, which your legs convert into mechanical energy that moves the bike's pedals.

Obtaining Chemical Energy

Figure 6 After this pika finishes its meal, the chemical reactions that occur during digestion will provide energy to the animal. Pikas are native to California and other parts of western North America.

Energy in Chemical Reactions

A student initiates two chemical reactions by adding a different substance to each of two beakers with different solutions. She observes them for 10 minutes, recording the temperature of the solution in each beaker every minute. She knows that a chemical reaction has occurred because the properties of the new substances are different than the properties of the original substances.

1. **SEP Use Mathematics** What was the temperature change of each solution after 10 minutes?

   ....

   ....

2. **SEP Interpret Data** Which of the beakers had a reaction that absorbed thermal energy? Which had a reaction that released thermal energy?

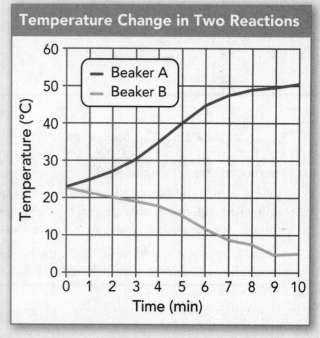

Temperature Change in Two Reactions

....

3. **SEP Communicate Information** Which solution could be used in a cooling pack to keep food and drinks cold in a cooler? Explain.

....

....

....

1. **Classify** A large bar of solid gold is melted into liquid. The liquid is then poured into molds to make a number of gold coins. Was this a chemical or physical change? Explain.

....

....

....

2. **Infer** If you cut an apple into slices and leave them in the open air, they will slowly turn brown. What kind of chemical change is shown by this change in properties? Explain.

....

....

....

3. **SEP Engage in Argument** A friend notices that a nail that was left outside for a few months seems larger and heavier than it was before. He says it disproves the law of conservation of mass. Explain why he is wrong.

....

....

....

....

4. **SEP Construct Explanations** Gray whales travel down California's coast as they migrate between cool waters off Alaska to the warmer waters along Mexico. In which area do you think more thermal energy would move from the whale to its environment? Explain.

....

....

....

....

....

....

....

5. **Summarize** A stick of butter is melted in a saucepan. As it continues to cook, the butter turns brown. What changes have occurred?

....

....

....

....

....

....

Quest CHECK-INS

In this lesson, you learned the difference between a physical change and a chemical change and how changes in energy are involved. You also learned about the conservation of mass.

Evaluate Why is it important to know the difference between chemical and physical changes when designing special effects?

....

....

....

....

....

INTERACTIVITY

Mysterious Movie Fog

HANDS-ON LAB

Cinematic Science

Go online to learn how "dry ice" and other substances are used to make physical and chemical changes in special effects.

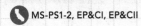
littleBits™

▶ **VIDEO**

Find out about maglev trains and how they work.

California's
Super Physicists

HOW do you improve existing technology? You engineer it!

➤ **The Challenge:** To develop practical applications for superconductors in medicine, communications, and transportation.

Phenomenon Superconductivity is a property of some substances, first observed in 1911, in which they lose all electrical resistance when they are cooled. At these low temperatures, certain elements and alloys become not just good conductors of electricity, but superconductors. This transition from a conductor to a superconductor is an important physical change! Once a material is superconducting, it can carry current more efficiently and also generate incredibly strong magnetic fields—strong enough to levitate a train on its track. More energy-efficient technologies can result in less demand for fossil fuels as well as the harmful effects of burning these limited resources.

In the last few decades, researchers have made significant breakthroughs in discovering other materials that show superconductivity at temperatures not quite as cold, which are less costly and complex to use. And now physicists at the University of California San Diego have engineered a device for controlling electric currents through these "high-temperature" superconductors. Their work paves the way for more sensitive medical devices, more efficient satellite communications, and other yet-to-be-discovered applications.

DESIGN CHALLENGE

Can you use magnets to build a model of a maglev train? Go to the Engineering Design Notebook to find out!

The surface below a magnet is cooled enough to become superconducting, allowing the magnet to levitate.

MS-PS1-1, MS-PS1-2,
EP&CIa, EP&CIIb

Evidence-Based Assessment

A group of students is developing models of simple molecules to represent particles that are too small to see. The models help them describe and classify matter. The materials they have are pipe cleaners along with red, blue, and yellow clay.

The students are modeling four molecules. The data for these molecules is presented in the table below.

Hydrogen	Hydrogen chloride	Ammonia	Nitrogen trichloride
2 hydrogen atoms	1 hydrogen atom	1 nitrogen atom	1 nitrogen atom
	1 chlorine atom	3 hydrogen atoms	3 chlorine atoms

The students' models of the first three molecules are shown, with one of the models constructed incorrectly.

1. **SEP Analyze Data** Based on the data and the first two models, which atom is represented by the red clay?

A. nitrogen   B. hydrogen

C. chlorine   D. oxygen

2. **SEP Use Models** Which of the following can be done using the students' models? Select all that apply.

☐ Visualize the atoms bonded within the molecules.

☐ Determine the thermal energy of a hydrogen chloride atom.

☐ Show that some molecules are not compounds.

☐ Demonstrate how elements can combine to form different types of matter.

3. **Differentiate** How does the hydrogen molecule compare to the other molecules? Complete the sentence by selecting the correct answer for each blank.

The hydrogen molecule is ....

A. similar

B. different

because ....

A. they are all compounds; made of different types of atoms

B. it is the only compound; made of one type of atom

4. **SEP Define Problems** Which model has been constructed incorrectly? Explain how you would fix it.

....
....
....
....
....
....
....
....

5. **SEP Construct Explanations** Review the table to determine which atoms are needed to model nitrogen trichloride. Complete the model by labeling the circles with the correct color. Then, draw lines to show the bonds.

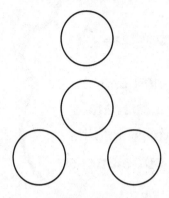

Quest FINDINGS

Complete the Quest!

Phenomenon Determine the best way to clearly present your ideas for the movie scene and the special effects that you would propose to the film director. You may present the storyboards or run through the actual scene as though it were being filmed.

Optimize Your Solution Are there any safety considerations or other issues that you encountered when demonstrating or discussing your special effects? How would they influence a redesign of your proposal?

....
....
....
....

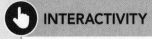

INTERACTIVITY

Reflect on Your Scene

EP&CIVb

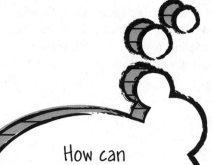

How can you **separate** a **mixture** into its pure **substances**?

Help Out the Wildlife

Background

Phenomenon Overnight, a materials storage facility was struck by a flash flood in Sierra County in northern California. The flood destroyed the building and washed salt, sand, and iron filings into a nearby pond. You wake up to a phone call from the Environmental Protection Agency asking if you can help clean up the contamination. Wildlife are at risk in the murky water. The owner of the storage facility also would like to recover as much salt, sand, and iron filings as possible. They should not go to waste!

Your job is to design a procedure to remove the salt, sand, and iron filings from the water.

Materials

(per group)

- 60-g mixture of salt, sand, and iron filings
- assorted materials and tools to separate the mixture

Safety

Be sure to follow all safety procedures provided by your teacher.

Murky Waters
Contaminated water can be a threat to the health of wildlife.

Sand, Salt, and Iron Filings

Plan Your Investigation

1. Your teacher will divide the class into groups and provide each group with some water and a mixture of salt, sand, and iron filings. Your mixture will contain the same quantities as other groups so that you can compare results.

2. Design a plan to separate the mixture into its components. You may want to consider some of these questions as you design your plan:

   - What materials can you use to separate each part of the mixture?

   - Are there other substances you can use to help you separate the mixture?

   - What order should your procedure follow in order to remove each part of the mixture?

   - What steps can you take to maximize the amount of each substance you recover from the mixture?

3. Identify the materials you will need to separate each substance in the mixture. Record your materials in the space provided below.

4. Develop your plan by creating a procedure. Record your procedure, paying careful attention to the order of the steps.

5. Finally, draw a data table in which you can record the mass of each substance that you recover and the material(s) that you used to do it.

HANDS-ON LAB

Demonstrate Go online for a downloadable worksheet of this lab.

Materials

....

....

....

....

Procedure

....

....

....

....

....

....

....

....

....

....

Observations

....

....

....

Data Table

Analyze and Interpret Data

1. **SEP Evaluate Information** Compare your results with another group. What were the similarities and differences in your findings?

....

....

....

....

....

2. **CCC Cause and Effect** What may be the causes of the differences in the masses recovered by each group?

....

....

....

....

....

3. **Apply Scientific Reasoning** What made you decide to do your procedural steps in the order in which you did them? Would any order have worked?

....

....

....

....

....

4. **SEP Design Solutions** Review the procedure and results of another group. If you were able to do the lab over again, what specific things would you do differently?

....

....

....

....

....

....

....

TOPIC

2

Solids, Liquids, and Gases

Investigative Phenomenon
How can a model be used to describe what happens to particles when thermal energy is added or removed?

MS-PS1-4 Develop a model that predicts and describes changes in particle motion, temperature, and state of a pure substance when thermal energy is added or removed.

EP&CIIb Students should be developing an understanding that methods used to extract, harvest, transport, and consume natural resources influence the geographic extent, composition, biological diversity, and viability of natural systems.

EP&CIVb Students should be developing an understanding that the byproducts of human activity are not readily prevented from entering natural systems and may be beneficial, neutral, or detrimental in their effect.

Why can you see this horse's breath in the cold?

HANDS-ON LAB

uConnect See if you can identify all the states of matter in three bottles.

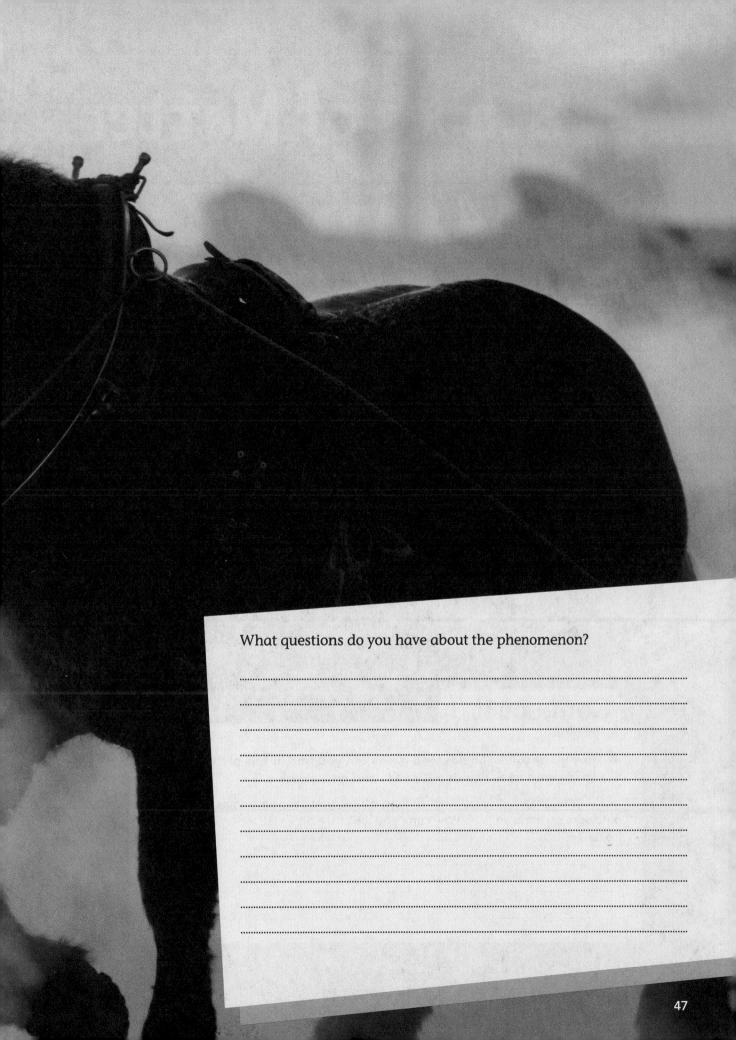

What questions do you have about the phenomenon?

....
....
....
....
....
....
....
....
....
....

HANDS-ON LAB

иInvestigate Distinguish between states of matter by understanding their properties.

MS-PS1-4 Develop a model that predicts and describes changes in particle motion, temperature, and state of a pure substance when thermal energy is added or removed.

Connect It!

✏️ **How many solids, liquids, and gases can you find in this picture? Label the solids with an S, liquids with an L, and gases with a G.**

SEP Construct Explanations During winter, you can sometimes ice skate outdoors on a frozen lake. Why can't you ice skate on a lake when it is not frozen?

....

....

....

Solids, Liquids, and Gases

Everything around you is made of matter. Matter exists in different forms, depending on a variety of factors, such as temperature. Most of it exists as molecules or other groups of atoms bound together. A few gases exist as single atoms that do not bind to other atoms.

Suppose you are taking a walk around a lake on a snowy day, such as in **Figure 1**. Everywhere you look, water is around you in different forms. It crunches loudly as snow beneath your feet. Liquid water on the surface of the lake flows freely when the wind blows. And invisible water particles exist in the air you breathe. The water around you is in three different phases of matter: solid, liquid, and gas.

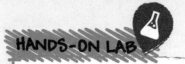

HANDS-ON LAB

ⓤ**Investigate** Distinguish between states of matter by understanding their properties.

Literacy Connection

Write Informative Texts Describe a solid, liquid, and gas found outdoors where you live.

....
....
....
....
....

Water Everywhere

Figure 1 In this summer morning scene of the Sierra Nevada Mountains in California, water exists in different forms.

Describing Solids

The ring box in **Figure 2** contains a ring made of pure silver. What would happen if you took the ring out of the box and placed it on your finger? Would it drip onto the floor? Of course not, because it's a solid. A **solid** has a definite shape and a definite volume. Remember that volume is the amount of space that matter fills. Volume is usually measured in cubic centimeters (cm^3), cubic meters (m^3), milliliters (mL), or liters (L).

A book is another example of a solid. If you place a book in your backpack, it will stay the same shape and size as it was before. A solid maintains its shape and volume in any position or container.

Particles of a Solid

The particles that make up a solid are packed very closely together, as shown in **Figure 2**. The particles are all identical, which means they make up a pure substance. This fixed, closely-packed arrangement of particles causes a solid to have a definite shape and volume. The particles in a solid are closely locked in position so that they cannot move around one another on their own. They can only **vibrate** in place, meaning they move back and forth slightly (see **Figure 3**).

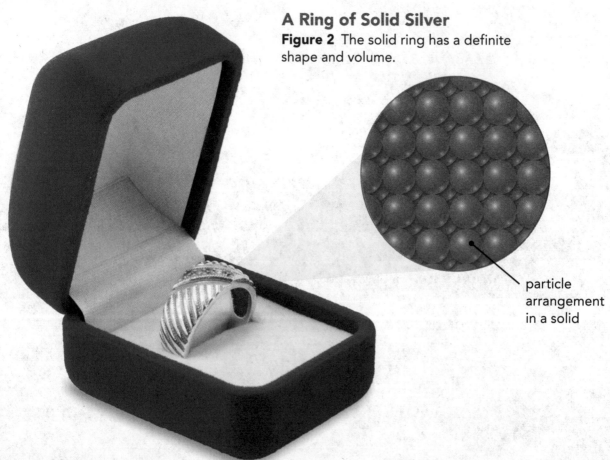

A Ring of Solid Silver
Figure 2 The solid ring has a definite shape and volume.

particle arrangement in a solid

Dancing In The Crowd
Figure 3 People at a packed concert don't move very far, but if they're having fun, they're not standing still, either! These people dancing in place are a lot like particles vibrating in a solid.

SEP Communicate Information Think about the motion of the particles in a solid and come up with your own way of describing them.

....
....
....
....
....

Physical Properties of Solids Of course, not all solids are the same. Some are hard and brittle, while some are flexible. Some have smooth surfaces and are heavy, while others are sharp and light. Take a look at the natural quartz and the eraser in **Figure 4**. These are both solids, but they are very different!

Comparing Solids
Figure 4 Determine Differences
Write down the differences that you notice in shape, structure, and texture between the quartz and the eraser.

Eraser
....
....
....

Quartz
....
....
....

Types of Solids The particles inside quartz are aligned in a regular, repeating pattern. This pattern creates crystals. Solids that are made up of crystals are called crystalline solids. Salt, sugar, and snow are examples of crystalline solids. When a crystalline solid is heated, it melts at a distinct temperature.

On the other hand, the material that makes up an eraser is an amorphous solid. In amorphous solids, such as the butter shown in **Figure 5**, the particles are not arranged in a regular pattern. Also, an amorphous solid does not melt at a distinct temperature. Glass is an example of an amorphous solid. It might look crystalline when it is cut into regular shapes, but it is amorphous because of its particle arrangement and the fact that it does not melt at a specific temperature. A glass blower can bend and shape glass that has been heated because it gradually becomes softer. Rubber and plastics are other examples of amorphous solids. They are very useful in manufacturing because they can be gradually heated and cooled to take specific, detailed shapes such as shoe soles and toys.

Model It !

Crystalline and Amorphous Solids

Figure 5 ✏ A pat of butter is an amorphous solid. The particles that make up the butter are not arranged in a regular pattern. The sapphire gem stones are crystalline solids. Draw what you think the particles look like in a crystalline solid.

☑ CHECK POINT Explain
In your own words, explain the main differences between crystalline solids and amorphous solids.

....

....

....

....

....

....

....

Describing Liquids

What happens when you spill a drink? It spreads into a wide, shallow puddle, as shown in **Figure 6**. Without a container, your drink does not have a definite shape. Like a solid, however, it does have a constant volume. Your drink is a liquid. A **liquid** has a definite volume but no shape of its own.

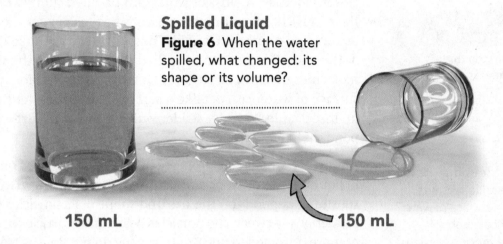

Spilled Liquid
Figure 6 When the water spilled, what changed: its shape or its volume?

....

150 mL   150 mL

Particles of a Liquid The particle model explains the difference between a solid and a liquid. In general, the particles in a liquid are always in contact with one another. They are packed almost as closely together as those in a solid. However, the particles in a liquid are not fixed in place. They can move around one another. You can compare this movement to a group of marbles in your hand. Like the particles of a liquid, the marbles slide around one another but still touch. Freely moving particles allow a liquid to flow from place to place. So a liquid is also called a fluid, meaning a "substance that flows." Because its particles are free to move, a liquid has no definite shape. However, it does have a definite volume, as shown in **Figure 7**.

Liquids Change Shape
Figure 7 These two pools hold the same volume of water even though they have different shapes. Liquids take the shape of their containers.

particle arrangement in a liquid

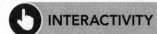
Make Meaning Have you ever seen leaves sitting on top of the surface of water? In your science notebook, describe the property of liquid water that allows the leaves to sit on its surface.

Surface Tension

Figure 8 Does this water strider have magic powers? No, it doesn't. Because of surface tension, the water strider is able to do the impossible: walk on water.

Physical Properties of Liquids
Substances can be classified by their characteristic properties—physical or chemical properties that remain the same no matter how large or small the sample. Two major characteristic properties of liquids are surface tension and viscosity.

Surface tension is an inward force, or pull, among the molecules in a liquid that brings the molecules on the surface closer together. A glass of water can be filled slightly above the rim without spilling over. That's because water molecules attract one another strongly. These attractions cause molecules at the water's surface to be pulled slightly toward the water molecules beneath its surface. Due to surface tension, the surface of water can act like a sort of skin. Surface tension lets an insect called a water strider walk on the calm surface of a pond, as in **Figure 8**.

Another characteristic property of matter that can be observed in liquids is viscosity, or a resistance to flowing. The viscosity of a substance depends on the size and shape of its particles and the attractions between the particles. When the particles are larger or more attracted to one another, they do not flow as freely. Liquids with high viscosities flow slowly. Honey is an example of a liquid with a very high viscosity (**Figure 9**). Liquids with low viscosity flow quickly. Water and vinegar have relatively low viscosities. Substances in other states of matter have viscosity as well. For example, solids have higher viscosity than liquids.

CHECK POINT **Write Informative Texts** Would honey be considered more viscous or less viscous than cranberry juice? Explain.

....

....

....

Viscous Honey
Figure 9 Honey flows slowly compared to many other liquids.

particle arrangement in a gas

Volume of a Gas
Figure 10 The volume of a gas depends on its container. The volume of the hot air in this balloon gliding over Napa Valley, California, is determined by the size of the balloon.

Describing Gases

The particle model explains the difference between a liquid and a gas. Like a liquid, a gas is a fluid. It has particles that can move around one another. However, unlike a liquid, a **gas** has neither a definite shape nor a definite volume. That's because the particles in a gas do not remain in contact with one another.

Particles of a Gas If you could see the particles that make up a gas, you would see them moving in all directions. They are widely spaced and collide with one another as they fly about. When a gas is in a closed container, the gas particles move and spread apart to fill the container.

Physical Properties of Gases Because gas particles fill all of the space available, the volume of a gas is the same as the volume of its container. For example, suppose you took the gas out of the hot air balloon in **Figure 10** and put it into another container. The volume of the gas would change, although the amount of the gas has not changed. In general, the particles of a gas flow more easily than the particles of a liquid, so gases have lower viscosity than liquids.

☑ CHECK POINT **Determine Central Ideas** What are the main differences between gases and liquids?

....

....

....

▶ **VIDEO**

Discover the fourth state of matter: plasma!

👆 **INTERACTIVITY**

Use what you have learned to identify states of matter and describe their particles.

55

☑ LESSON 1 Check

1. **Identify** What two properties of a gas depend on its container?

....
....
....
....
....
....

2. **Determine Differences** How do liquids with a high viscosity differ from liquids with a low viscosity?

....
....
....
....
....
....

3. **CCC Energy and Matter** What are the similarities and differences of the particle motion in solids and liquids?

....
....
....
....
....
....

4. **CCC Cause and Effect** How do the particles in a liquid create surface tension?

....
....
....
....
....
....
....
....
....
....
....
....

5. **SEP Develop Models** 🖉 Based on what you have learned, draw models of the particles in a solid, a liquid, and a gas. Use dots for particles and arrows to show motion.

Solid   **Liquid**

Gas

🕐 MS-PS1-4

From "Ink" to Objects:
3-D PRINTING

👆 **INTERACTIVITY**

Find out about the technology and uses of 3-D printing.

When you hear the word *printing*, you probably think of words and images on paper. But 3-D printing has little to do with books!

The Challenge: To utilize the properties of solids and liquids to make 3-D objects.

Phenomenon Have you ever seen 3-D printing? Unlike traditional printing, which simply binds ink onto paper or or some other material, 3-D printing makes physical shapes that have mass and volume. How do these printers work?

Remember what you have learned about solids and liquids. In liquids, particles can move and slide past one another, while in solids, particles are fixed in place and only vibrate. This gives liquids and solids their unique properties. However, these properties can be changed by applying energy, such as heat.

Think of what happens when you melt butter. You take the butter, which is a solid, and apply heat, melting the butter into a new form—a liquid. 3-D printers work in the same way. They take a solid material, usually a plastic or a metal, and apply heat until the material melts into a liquid. Then, the liquid is sprayed or squeezed onto a platform, according to a design that has been programmed into the printer. The liquid material hardens again into a solid. After many layers build up, a 3-D object is completed.

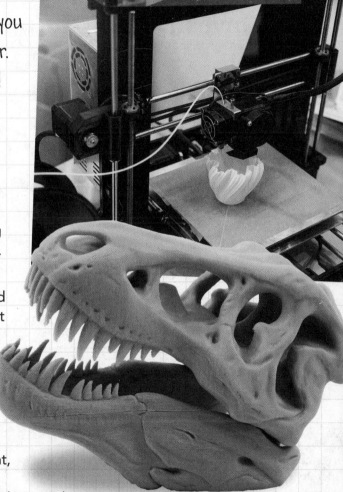

3-D printers can make complex 3-D objects quickly and easily. They are useful in a wide variety of production industries!

DESIGN CHALLENGE

What could you design with a 3-D printer? Go to the Engineering Design Notebook to find out!

② Changes of State

HANDS-ON LAB

иInvestigate Understand why fog can sometimes form on a mirror.

MS-PS1-4 Develop a model that predicts and describes changes in particle motion, temperature, and state of a pure substance when thermal energy is added or removed.

Connect It!

✏ **If you've ever watched a burning candle, you've seen how the solid wax melts into a liquid. Circle an area in the picture where you see this happening.**

CCC Stability and Change When the liquid wax cools, it hardens. How is wax hardening similar to liquid water turning to ice?

....

....

....

Thermal Energy and Temperature

You have seen substances change state. For example, snow melts into liquid water, puddles of rain freeze in the cold, and boiling water becomes steam. What do all of these changes have in common? They involve a change in the thermal energy and temperature of the substance. Thermal energy and temperature are related, but they are not the same thing. You can understand them in terms of the particle model of matter.

Thermal Energy Particles have both kinetic energy and potential energy. Kinetic energy is energy of motion, and potential energy is energy that is stored. **Thermal energy** is the total internal kinetic and potential energy of all the particles in an object or substance.

You can increase the thermal energy of a substance by heating it. When you apply heat, you are transferring energy from the heat source to the substance. If you add enough energy to the substance, it can become hot enough to change its state of matter, like the candle wax in **Figure 1**.

Note that in everyday language, the term *heat* can be used to describe the thermal energy contained in an object. However, when scientists use the term *heat*, they are referring only to energy that is transferred between two objects or systems at different temperatures.

Temperature Recall that all particles of matter are constantly moving. **Temperature** is proportional to the average kinetic and potential energy of the particles in an object or substance. The faster the particles are moving, the greater their kinetic energy, and the higher the temperature.

A thermometer measures temperature in degrees, such as degrees Celsius (°C) or degrees Fahrenheit (°F). The thermometer registers a higher temperature when particles are moving faster. How do you make particles speed up? Heat a substance, such as the cider in **Figure 2**, so that its thermal energy increases and its particles move faster. As a result, the temperature of the substance will increase. On the other hand, when a substance is cooled and its thermal energy decreases, its particles slow down. The temperature of the substance decreases.

Hot Apple Cider
Figure 2 Apple cider is best served hot!

☑ CHECK POINT
Integrate with Visuals
✎ Draw an arrow on **Figure 2** to show the direction of heat flow. Label the apple cider's thermal energy as increasing or decreasing.

Dripping Candles
Figure 1 The candle wax experiences a change of state as it melts.

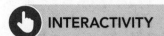

INTERACTIVITY

Examine how particles move and how temperature changes when thermal energy increases or decreases.

Changes of State Between Solid and Liquid

Have you ever let a bar of chocolate sit in a car too long on a hot day? If so, you know what it looks like when the chocolate melts. Some of the solid bar changes to liquid.

Melting When the temperature of most solids increases enough, they change to liquid. The change in state from a solid to a liquid is called melting. This change of state involves an increase in thermal energy. In general, particles of a liquid have more thermal energy than particles of the same substance in solid form.

In pure, crystalline solids, melting occurs at a specific temperature, called the **melting point**. **Figure 3** shows what happens to the temperature of an ice cube after it is taken from the freezer and left out at room temperature. At first, the energy flowing from the environment into the ice makes the water molecules vibrate faster, raising the temperature of the ice cube. At a solid's melting point, its particles vibrate so fast that they break free from their fixed positions. When the ice cube reaches the melting point of water, 0°C, its temperature stops increasing. At this point, added energy continues to change the arrangement of the water molecules from ice crystals into liquid water as the ice melts.

Because the melting point is a characteristic property of a substance, chemists often compare melting points when trying to identify an unknown material. For example, silver and iron are both shiny metals with a similar color. The melting point of silver is 961.8°C, while the melting point of iron is 1,538°C. No matter how much of a substance there is, it will always melt at the same temperature.

Student Discourse

Have you ever eaten an ice cream cone on a hot summer day? With a classmate, discuss what happened to the ice cream. In your science notebook, describe the cause and effect in the process.

Changing Ice Into Water

Figure 3 The graph shows how the temperature of solid ice changes as it melts into liquid water.

1. SEP Interpret Data How long did it take for the ice to completely melt once it reached the melting point?

2. SEP Develop Models Complete the labels for Solid and Liquid. Write a few words to describe the motion of the particles in each state.

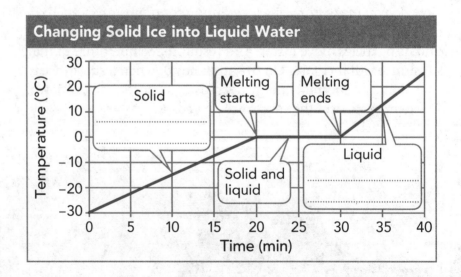

Changing Solid Ice into Liquid Water

Freezing You have probably seen many substances freeze. When you put liquid water into a freezer, for example, it turns to solid ice. The thermal energy of the liquid water decreases and the water molecules move more slowly. At 0°C, the water molecules begin to become fixed in place, and the liquid water turns to solid ice.

Freezing is the change of state from a liquid to a solid. It is the reverse of melting. Unlike water, some substances do not have to be cold to the touch in order to freeze. For example, some types of wax freeze at 63°C, which is greater than the highest surface temperature ever recorded on Earth. A substance's **freezing point** is simply the temperature at which it changes from a liquid to a solid. So, water's freezing point is 0°C, and the wax's freezing point is 63°C. It doesn't matter how much of a substance there is—it will always have the same freezing point.

✓ CHECK POINT **Determine Central Ideas** What is the difference between melting and freezing?

....

....

....

The Freezing Point

The graph shows a substance changing from liquid to solid.

1. SEP Interpret Data Based on the graph, what is the value of the freezing point for this substance?

....

2. Draw Comparative Inferences Think about what would happen if this substance were in the solid phase first and then melted into a liquid. What would you say about the solid's melting point compared to the liquid's freezing point?

....

....

....

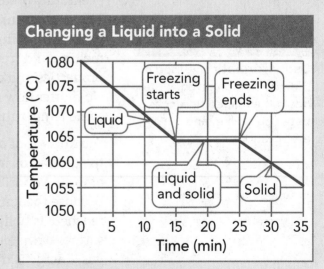

Changing a Liquid into a Solid

3. Identify ✎ The following are four substances and their melting points. Which substance does the graph represent? Circle your answer.

Platinum: 1768.3°C   Gold: 1064.18°C   Silver: 961.78°C   Mercury: −38.83°C

Evaporation or Boiling?

Figure 4 Examples of vaporization are all around us.

Identify Label each picture as boiling, evaporation, or both.

INTERACTIVITY

Observe and describe the motion of particles in substances at different temperatures.

Literacy Connection

Use Information Based on the information given, write down the main differences between boiling and evaporation.

....

....

....

....

....

....

....

Changes of State Between Liquid and Gas

Why does a pot of hot soup create steam? How does fog form? To answer these questions, you need to look at what happens when changes occur between the liquid and gas states.

Evaporation and Boiling The change in state from a liquid to a gas is called **vaporization** (vay puhr ih ZAY shun). Vaporization occurs when the particles in a liquid gain enough energy to move independently and away from each other. There are two main types of vaporization—boiling and evaporation.

Vaporization that takes place both below and at the surface of a liquid is called boiling. When soup boils, vaporized soup molecules form bubbles below the surface. The bubbles rise and eventually break the surface of the liquid, as shown in **Figure 4**. The temperature at which a liquid boils is called its **boiling point**. The boiling point of water is 100°C at sea level. As with melting and freezing points, boiling points are characteristic properties and can be used to identify unknown substances. No matter how much of a substance you have, it will boil at the same temperature.

You know that a rain puddle eventually disappears from the ground as it changes from a liquid to a gas. The puddle of water vaporizes, so why don't we see the water boiling? Because the temperature of the water in the puddle has not reached its boiling point, only the water particles on the surface of the puddle have enough energy to turn into a gas. Energy is transferred to these particles from the sun's radiation and the surrounding air. Vaporization that takes place only on the surface of a liquid is called **evaporation**. The process continues until all of the particles evaporate and the puddle is gone. While boiling occurs only at one temperature, evaporation can occur at all temperatures.

The Effect of Pressure When you push on an object, you apply pressure to the object. The pressure depends on the force you apply and the area over which you apply the force.

$$\text{Pressure} = \frac{\text{Force}}{\text{Area}}$$

Gas particles constantly collide with one another and with any nearby surfaces. As a result, a gas pushes on these surfaces. The pressure a gas applies is greater if its particles collide with a surface more often, as shown in **Figure 5**. The particles are all identical, so the figure represents a pure substance.

The air that surrounds you is constantly applying pressure to you. This pressure, called atmospheric pressure, can affect how easily a liquid changes to a gas. Think about boiling water to make pasta. Atmospheric pressure is acting on the surface of the liquid water. As the water is heated on the stove, the pressure inside the liquid increases. When the pressure inside the liquid equals the atmospheric pressure, the liquid boils.

In locations high above sea level—such as Denver, Colorado—the atmospheric pressure is less because the air is less dense. This means that it takes less thermal energy to get a liquid to boil in these locations. In Denver, water boils at 95°C.

Pressure and Vaporization

Figure 5 🖊 Circle the image in which the liquid would require more thermal energy to change to a gas. How did you determine your answer?

....

....

....

....

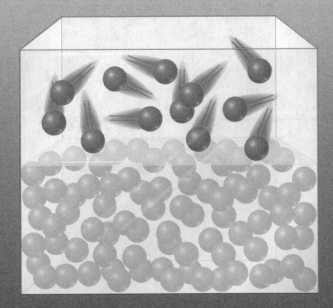 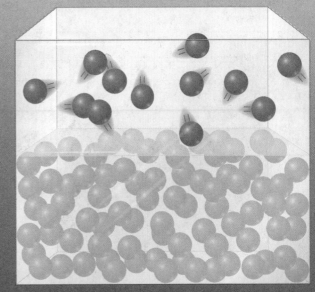

HANDS-ON LAB

☑**Investigate** Understand why fog can sometimes form on a mirror.

Academic Vocabulary

In orange juice, bits of pulp are suspended in liquid. Explain what you think *suspended* means.

....

....

....

....

....

Condensation The reverse of vaporization is condensation. **Condensation** is the change in state from a gas to a liquid. It occurs when particles in a gas lose enough thermal energy to change state.

You can observe condensation by breathing onto a window, as shown in **Figure 6**. When warm water vapor in your breath reaches the cooler surface of the window, the water vapor condenses into liquid droplets.

Have you ever wondered how fog forms? Much like clouds in the atmosphere, fog forms (**Figure 7**) when water vapor in the air condenses into tiny liquid droplets. Water vapor is a colorless gas that you cannot see. The steam you see above a kettle of boiling water is not water vapor, and neither are clouds or fog. What you see in those cases are tiny droplets of liquid water **suspended** in air.

Condensation on a Window

Figure 6 Warm breath condenses on the cool surface of a window.

Foggy Bay

Figure 7 Fog is a common occurrence around the San Francisco Bay Area in California. It forms as the air around the city is cooled by the water in the bay.

☑ **CHECK POINT** **Draw Evidence** What is happening to the water vapor in the air in this photograph?

....

....

Changing State from Solid to Gas

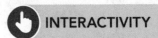

INTERACTIVITY

Draw conclusions about how thermal energy affects particle motion, temperature, and state.

In places where the winters are very cold, the snow may disappear even when the temperature stays well below freezing. This change is the result of sublimation. **Sublimation** occurs when the surface particles of a solid gain enough energy that they form a gas. During sublimation, particles of a solid do not pass through the liquid state as they form a gas.

One example of sublimation occurs with dry ice, which is solid carbon dioxide. At ordinary atmospheric pressures, carbon dioxide cannot exist as a liquid. So instead of melting, solid carbon dioxide changes directly into a gas, as shown in **Figure 8**. As it sublimes, the carbon dioxide absorbs thermal energy from its surroundings. For this reason, dry ice can be used to keep materials cold. Some fog machines use dry ice to create fog in movies. When dry ice becomes a gas, it cools water vapor in the nearby air. The water vapor then condenses into a liquid, forming fog near the dry ice.

VIDEO

Watch a video about changes of state.

Model It

Dry Ice

Figure 8 Dry ice sublimes, changing directly from a solid to a gas.

SEP Develop Models ✏ Think about what is happening to the particles of carbon dioxide as the dry ice changes from solid to gas. Draw models of the particles in the two phases of matter. Use an arrow to show the flow of thermal energy into the solid carbon dioxide. Write an explanation of how the temperature changes and how the motion of the molecules changes as the dry ice becomes a gas.

☑ LESSON 2 Check

1. CCC Cause and Effect What is the main cause of any change of state?

....
....
....
....
....
....

2. SEP Construct Explanations If there is high gas pressure above a liquid, what can you say about the amount of thermal energy required for the liquid to change to gas?

....
....
....
....
....
....
....

3. Compare and Contrast In terms of changes in particle motion and thermal energy, how does condensation differ from evaporation?

....
....
....
....
....
....
....
....

4. Predict Phenomena If you left a block of dry ice in a bowl at room temperature all day, what would happen to it? How does the particle model account for what happens to this natural system?

....
....
....
....
....
....
....
....
....
....
....

5. CCC Energy and Matter Solid substance A has a melting point of 100°C. Liquid substance B has a freezing point of 110°C. For each substance, identify its state of matter and describe the motion of its particles when the substance is at 115°C.

....
....
....
....
....
....
....
....

 MS-PS1-4

FREEZE that Scalpel!

How do refrigerators and freezers keep food from spoiling? They circulate chilled air. The cold temperatures prevent bacteria from forming.

Cryosurgery works in a similar way. It uses extremely cold temperatures to treat cancers, pre-cancerous growths, warts, moles, and skin infections.

While refrigerators and freezers use specially engineered gases to keep food cold, cryosurgery generally uses liquid nitrogen to freeze unwanted, harmful cells. At room temperature, nitrogen is a colorless, odorless gas. However, when it becomes extremely cold, it condenses into a liquid. To achieve this state, the nitrogen has to be cooled to around −200°C! At this temperature, liquid nitrogen instantly freezes anything it touches, and with human tissue, it can destroy cells upon contact.

In cryosurgery, new techniques are being developed every day. For example, some doctors have started using liquefied argon gas, rather than liquid nitrogen, because it allows for even faster freezing of cells. Researchers are also exploring ways to use cryosurgery safely to target cells from the inside, instead of from outside the body. Both medical doctors and engineers take part in developing new techniques. For either sort of career, studying science is an important first step.

VIDEO

Discover how planes form vapor trails in the sky.

MY DISCOVERY

Type "cryosurgery" into an online search engine to learn more about this technology and the conditions it can treat. Find out what California and U.S. government agencies regulate medical treatments.

Liquid nitrogen freeze technique treats a skin cancer.

Cryosurgery is used to kill tumors that cannot be reached and cut out.

Skin lesion

Liquid nitrogen

MS-PS1-4

Evidence-Based Assessment

On a sunny morning, Skyler's father fills his new swimming pool with water from a garden hose. The following day, he notices that the water level has dropped—there is less water in the pool than there was the day before. He checks the pool for any leaks, but he finds nothing.

Skyler has a hunch as to why the water level has dropped. He draws some models to help explain what has happened.

Model 1:

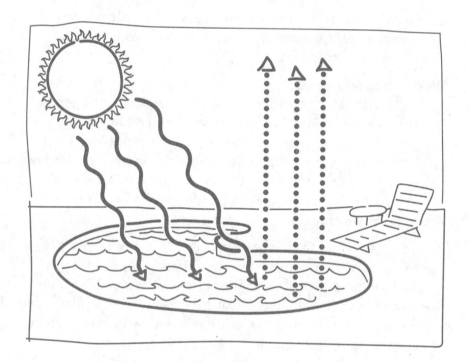

Model 2:

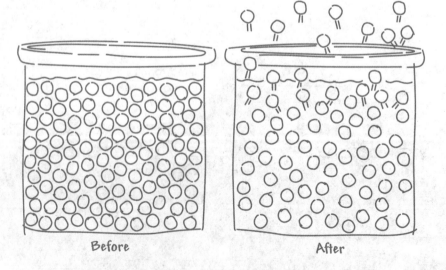

Before   After

1. **Identify** What change of state is Skyler representing with his models?

   A. condensation   **B.** evaporation

   C. sublimation   **D.** melting

2. **SEP Use Models** Look at Model 1. What do the lines from the sun to the water represent? What do the dotted lines coming from the surface of the water represent?

   ....

   ....

   ....

   ....

   ....

   ....

   ....

   ....

   ....

   ....

   ....

   ....

   ....

   ....

3. **SEP Develop Models** Circle the words to show how you could improve Model 1 by adding more labels.

   To improve this model, label the lines from the sun as (heat / water vapor / air molecules). Label the dotted lines rising from the pool as (heat / water vapor / molecules).

4. **SEP Cite Evidence** Describe what is happening to the thermal energy of the water in the pool during the day. Use evidence from the models to explain your answer.

   ....

   ....

   ....

   ....

   ....

   ....

   ....

   ....

   ....

   ....

   ....

   ....

   ....

5. **Draw Comparative Inferences** Complete the table to describe properties of matter and energy in the "After" picture of Model 2.

	States of Matter	Kinetic Energy (↑ or ↓)	Temperature (↑ or ↓)
After			

MS-PS1-4

Melting ICE

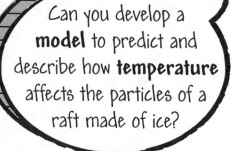

Can you develop a **model** to predict and describe how **temperature** affects the particles of a raft made of ice?

Background

Phenomenon Off the coast of Alaska, your ship has sunk, but you manage to survive by climbing on an iceberg. You need a raft to float to the mainland. The only things available are floes, which are sheets of ice. The liquid water temperature is warmer than the ice, so your raft is going to melt as you travel! The iceberg formed from snow, so it is pure water. The sea ice formed from seawater, so it contains some salt. The sea ice is a mixture, not a pure substance.

In this investigation, you will use two ice cubes to explore how the temperature of liquid water affects how quickly ice melts. Gather evidence to conclude how long an ice raft will last in two cases: where the liquid water temperature is 40–45°C, and where the liquid water temperature is 20–25°C.

Materials

(per group)

- stopwatch or timer
- thermometer
- 2 plastic cups
- 2 plastic spoons
- 2 ice cubes, about 2 cm on each side
- warm water, 40–45°C
- room-temperature water, 20–25°C

Safety

Follow all safety guidelines provided by your teacher.

Design an Investigation

1. Begin by making a prediction about the results of the experiment using your background knowledge of ice. Include how long you think it will take each ice cube to melt completely into a liquid. Apply your prediction to your ice raft situation: assuming the mainland is far enough away that it would take 5 minutes for you to float there, would your raft stay solid long enough in 40–45°C water? In 20–25°C water?

....

....

....

....

HANDS-ON LAB

и**Demonstrate** Go online for a downloadable worksheet of this lab.

2. Next, design, develop, and conduct an experiment to test your prediction. Use the space below to sketch, and the next page to write, your procedure. Think about these questions when designing your experiment.

- How might the size of the ice cubes affect your results?

- Will the amount of water in each cup affect your results?

- Would the motion of the ice cube affect your results?

- How might you move the ice cube to model the raft's motion?

- What factors will be controls in your experiment?

3. In addition to writing your procedure, design a data table to record your observations and measurements. Be sure to use the correct metric units in your data table.

4. Tell your teacher your hypothesis and describe your procedure. Once your procedure is approved, run your experiment and record your results in the data table.

Procedure

....
....
....
....
....
....
....
....
....
....
....
....
....
....

Data Table

Analyze and Interpret Data

1. **Predict** Were your predictions about the ice cubes supported by the results of the experiment? Explain why or why not.

   ....

   ....

   ....

2. **SEP Interpret Data** In which cup did the liquid water temperature change the most? Discuss your results.

   ....

   ....

   ....

   ....

3. **SEP Construct Explanations** When the ice melted, its particles gained enough energy to overcome the forces holding them together as solid ice. What was the source of that energy?

   ....

   ....

4. **Identify Limitations** In what ways did the experiment accurately reflect icebergs melting in ocean water? In what ways did the experiment simplify the real-word scenario?

   ....

   ....

   ....

5. **SEP Develop Models** In the space provided, draw two models or diagrams to show the arrangement of particles in the ice before and after thermal energy was added. For each model, identify the temperature and the state of matter.

Conduct an Investigation

Evidence **Now that you have completed both topics within this segment, do the following tasks.**

Communicate Collaboratively With a partner, discuss what you have learned in this segment and how it relates to the matter that makes up both living and nonliving things. Then use evidence from this segment to complete the Venn diagram by comparing and contrasting the matter that makes up living things and nonliving things.

Matter

Matter in
Living Things

Matter in
Nonliving Things

Atomic Analysis

Case Study Now that you've learned about what makes up matter and the properties of matter, you will research two examples of compounds: glucose and calcium carbonate. For each compound, you will design and complete a chemical composition card using a word processing or graphics program.

On the front of each card, include the name of the compound and an image of the compound in its solid state. On the back of each card, use the results of your research to list the following information for each compound:

- Name of the compound
- Physical properties
- Elements that make up the compound, including their chemical symbols
- Properties of each of these elements
- Whether the compound is found in living or nonliving things, and what purpose it serves for these things
- Either a drawing or a description of the structure of the compound, including the correct number of each type of atom contained in a unit of the compound

To finish up, think about which compound is found in a tufa tower and which one is found in a toad. Add an image of a tufa tower on the front of the appropriate card and an image of a Great Basin spadefoot toad on the front of the other card.

Both glucose and calcium carbonate are white, powdery compounds in their solid states.

Glucose

Calcium carbonate

Based on your research, answer the following questions.

1. **CCC Structure and Function** Describe each number and type of atom in a molecule of calcium carbonate. How do the properties of these elements compare to the properties of the compound?

   ....

   ....

   ....

   ....

   ....

2. **SEP Construct Explanations** One physical property of a compound is its solubility, or how easily it dissolves in water. From what you know about glucose and calcium carbonate, which one do you think has greater solubility? Justify your answer.

   ....

   ....

   ....

   ....

   ....

   ....

3. **SEP Cite Evidence** Suppose you are given a 20-g sample of one of the compounds you researched. You find the volume of the sample to be 13 cm^3. Is the sample glucose or is it calcium carbonate? Justify your answer. (The density of glucose is 1.54 g/cm^3, and the density of calcium carbonate is 2.71 g/cm^3.)

   ....

   ....

   ....

4. **CCC Cause and Effect** How does evaporation play a role in the distribution and different kinds of matter found in Mono Lake?

   ....

   ....

   ....

   ....

Use this space for recording notes and sketching out ideas.

🕐 SEP.1, SEP.8

The Meaning of Science

Science Skills

📓 **Reflect** Think about a time you misplaced something and could not find it. Write a sentence defining the problem. What science skills could you use to solve the problem? Explain how you would use at least three of the skills in the table.

Science is a way of learning about the natural world. It involves asking questions, making predictions, and collecting information to see if the answer is right or wrong.

The table lists some of the skills that scientists use. You use some of these skills every day. For example, you may observe and evaluate your lunch options before choosing what to eat.

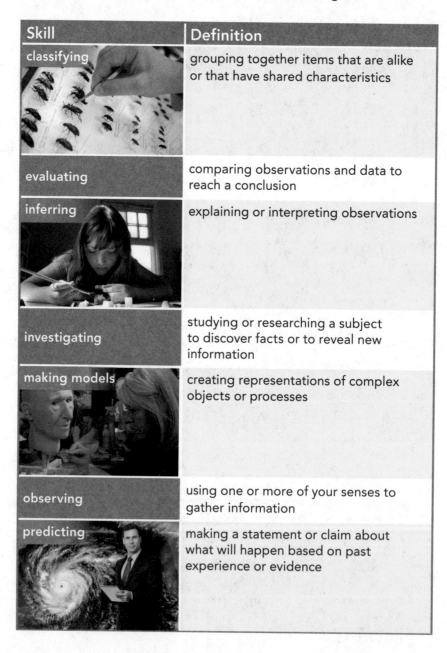

Skill	Definition
classifying	grouping together items that are alike or that have shared characteristics
evaluating	comparing observations and data to reach a conclusion
inferring	explaining or interpreting observations
investigating	studying or researching a subject to discover facts or to reveal new information
making models	creating representations of complex objects or processes
observing	using one or more of your senses to gather information
predicting	making a statement or claim about what will happen based on past experience or evidence

Scientific Attitudes

Curiosity often drives scientists to learn about the world around them. Creativity is useful for coming up with inventive ways to solve problems. Such qualities and attitudes, and the ability to keep an open mind, are essential for scientists.

When sharing results or findings, honesty and ethics are also essential. Ethics refers to rules for knowing right from wrong.

Being skeptical is also important. This means having doubts about things based on past experiences and evidence. Skepticism helps to prevent accepting data and results that may not be true.

Scientists must also avoid bias—likes or dislikes of people, ideas, or things. They must avoid experimental bias, which is a mistake that may make an experiment's preferred outcome more likely.

Scientific Reasoning

Scientific reasoning depends on being logical and objective. When you are objective, you use evidence and apply logic to draw conclusions. Being subjective means basing conclusions on personal feelings, biases, or opinions. Subjective reasoning can interfere with science and skew results. Objective reasoning helps scientists use observations to reach conclusions about the natural world.

Scientists use two types of objective reasoning: deductive and inductive. Deductive reasoning involves starting with a general idea or theory and applying it to a situation. For example, the theory of plate tectonics indicates that earthquakes happen mostly where tectonic plates meet. You could then draw the conclusion, or deduce, that California has many earthquakes because tectonic plates meet there.

In inductive reasoning, you make a generalization from a specific observation. When scientists collect data in an experiment and draw a conclusion based on that data, they use inductive reasoning. For example, if fertilizer causes one set of plants to grow faster than another, you might infer that the fertilizer promotes plant growth.

Make Meaning

Think about a bias the marine biologist in the photo could show that results in paying more or less attention to one kind of organism over others. Make a prediction about how that bias could affect the biologist's survey of the coral reef.

Write About It

Suppose it is raining when you go to sleep one night. When you wake up the next morning, you observe frozen puddles on the ground and icicles on tree branches. Use scientific reasoning to draw a conclusion about the air temperature outside. Support your conclusion using deductive or inductive reasoning.

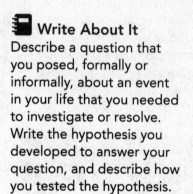

SEP.1, SEP.2, SEP.3, SEP.4, CCC.4

Science Processes

Scientific Inquiry

Scientists contribute to scientific knowledge by conducting investigations and drawing conclusions. The process often begins with an observation that leads to a question, which is then followed by the development of a hypothesis. This is known as scientific inquiry.

One of the first steps in scientific inquiry is asking questions. However, it's important to make a question specific with a narrow focus so the investigation will not be too broad. A biologist may want to know all there is to know about wolves, for example. But a good, focused question for a specific inquiry might be "How many offspring does the average female wolf produce in her lifetime?"

A hypothesis is a possible answer to a scientific question. A hypothesis must be testable. For something to be testable, researchers must be able to carry out an investigation and gather evidence that will either support or disprove the hypothesis.

Scientific Models

Models are tools that scientists use to study phenomena indirectly. A model is any representation of an object or process. Illustrations, dioramas, globes, diagrams, computer programs, and mathematical equations are all examples of scientific models. For example, a diagram of Earth's crust and mantle can help you to picture layers deep below the surface and understand events such as volcanic eruptions.

Models also allow scientists to represent objects that are either very large, such as our solar system, or very small, such as a molecule of DNA. Models can also represent processes that occur over a long period of time, such as the changes that have occurred throughout Earth's history.

Models are helpful, but they have limitations. Physical models are not made of the same materials as the objects they represent. Most models of complex objects or processes show only major parts, stages, or relationships. Many details are left out. Therefore, you may not be able to learn as much from models as you would through direct observation.

Reflect Identify the benefits and limitations of using a plastic model of DNA, as shown here.

Science Experiments

An experiment or investigation must be well planned to produce valid results. In planning an experiment, you must identify the independent and dependent variables. You must also do as much as possible to remove the effects of other variables. A controlled experiment is one in which you test only one variable at a time.

For example, suppose you plan a controlled experiment to learn how the type of material affects the speed at which sound waves travel through it. The only variable that should change is the type of material. This way, if the speed of sound changes, you know that it is a result of a change in the material, not another variable such as the thickness of the material or the type of sound used.

You should also remove bias from any investigation. You may inadvertently introduce bias by selecting subjects you like and avoiding those you don't like. Scientists often conduct investigations by taking random samples to avoid ending up with biased results.

Once you plan your investigation and begin to collect data, it's important to record and organize the data. You may wish to use a graph to display and help you to interpret the data.

Communicating is the sharing of ideas and results with others through writing and speaking. Communicating data and conclusions is a central part of science.

Scientists share knowledge, including new findings, theories, and techniques for collecting data. Conferences, journals, and websites help scientists to communicate with each other. Popular media, including newspapers, magazines, and social media sites, help scientists to share their knowledge with nonscientists. However, before the results of investigations are shared and published, other scientists should review the experiment for possible sources of error, such as bias and unsupported conclusions.

Write About It

List four ways you could communicate the results of a scientific study about the health of sea turtles in the Pacific Ocean.

SEP.1, SEP.6, SEP.7, SEP.8

Scientific Knowledge

Scientific Explanations

Suppose you learn that adult flamingos are pink because of the food they eat. This statement is a scientific explanation—it describes how something in nature works or explains why it happens. Scientists from different fields use methods such as researching information, designing experiments, and making models to form scientific explanations. Scientific explanations often result from many years of work and multiple investigations conducted by many scientists.

Scientific Theories and Laws

A scientific law is a statement that describes what you can expect to occur every time under a particular set of conditions. A scientific law describes an observed pattern in nature, but it does not attempt to explain it. For example, the law of superposition describes what you can expect to find in terms of the ages of layers of rock. Geologists use this observed pattern to determine the relative ages of sedimentary rock layers. But the law does not explain why the pattern occurs.

By contrast, a scientific theory is a well-tested explanation for a wide range of observations or experimental results. It provides details and describes causes of observed patterns. Something is elevated to a theory only when there is a large body of evidence that supports it. However, a scientific theory can be changed or overturned when new evidence is found.

Write About It
Choose two fields of science that interest you. Describe a method used to develop scientific explanations in each field.

SEP Construct Explanations Complete the table to compare and contrast a scientific theory and a scientific law.

	Scientific Theory	Scientific Law
Definition		
Does it attempt to explain a pattern observed in nature?		

Analyzing Scientific Explanations

To analyze scientific explanations that you hear on the news or read in a book such as this one, you need scientific literacy. Scientific literacy means understanding scientific terms and principles well enough to ask questions, evaluate information, and make decisions. Scientific reasoning gives you a process to apply. This includes looking for bias and errors in the research, evaluating data, and identifying faulty reasoning. For example, by evaluating how a survey was conducted, you may find a serious flaw in the researchers' methods.

Evidence and Opinions

The basis for scientific explanations is empirical evidence. Empirical evidence includes the data and observations that have been collected through scientific processes. Satellite images, photos, and maps of mountains and volcanoes are all examples of empirical evidence that support a scientific explanation about Earth's tectonic plates. Scientists look for patterns when they analyze this evidence. For example, they might see a pattern that mountains and volcanoes often occur near tectonic plate boundaries.

To evaluate scientific information, you must first distinguish between evidence and opinion. In science, evidence includes objective observations and conclusions that have been repeated. Evidence may or may not support a scientific claim. An opinion is a subjective idea that is formed from evidence, but it cannot be confirmed by evidence.

Write About It

Suppose the conservation committee of a town wants to gauge residents' opinions about a proposal to stock the local ponds with fish every spring. The committee pays for a survey to appear on a web site that is popular with people who like to fish. The results of the survey show 78 people in favor of the proposal and two against it. Do you think the survey's results are valid? Explain.

Make Meaning

Explain what empirical evidence the photograph reveals.

SEP.3, SEP.4

Tools of Science

Measurement

Making measurements using standard units is important in all fields of science. This allows scientists to repeat and reproduce other experiments, as well as to understand the precise meaning of the results of others. Scientists use a measurement system called the International System of Units, or SI.

For each type of measurement, there is a series of units that are greater or less than each other. The unit a scientist uses depends on what is being measured. For example, a geophysicist tracking the movements of tectonic plates may use centimeters, as plates tend to move small amounts each year. Meanwhile, a marine biologist might measure the movement of migrating bluefin tuna on the scale of kilometers.

Units for length, mass, volume, and density are based on powers of ten—a meter is equal to 100 centimeters or 1000 millimeters. Units of time do not follow that pattern. There are 60 seconds in a minute, 60 minutes in an hour, and 24 hours in a day. These units are based on patterns that humans perceived in nature. Units of temperature are based on scales that are set according to observations of nature. For example, 0°C is the temperature at which pure water freezes, and 100°C is the temperature at which it boils.

Write About It

Suppose you are planning an investigation in which you must measure the dimensions of several small mineral samples that fit in your hand. Which metric unit or units will you most likely use? Explain your answer.

Measurement	Metric units
Length or distance	meter (m), kilometer (km), centimeter (cm), millimeter (mm) 1 km = 1,000 m 1 cm = 10 mm 1 m = 100 cm
Mass	kilogram (kg), gram (g), milligram (mg) 1 kg = 1,000 g 1 g = 1,000 mg
Volume	cubic meter (m^3), cubic centimeter (cm^3) 1 m^3 = 1,000,000 cm^3
Density	kilogram per cubic meter (kg/m^3), gram per cubic centimeter (g/cm^3) 1,000 kg/m^3 = 1 g/cm^3
Temperature	degrees Celsius (°C), kelvin (K) 1°C = 273 K
Time	hour (h), minute (m), second (s)

Math Skills

Using numbers to collect and interpret data involves math skills that are essential in science. For example, you use math skills when you estimate the number of birds in an entire forest after counting the actual number of birds in ten trees.

Scientists evaluate measurements and estimates for their precision and accuracy. In science, an accurate measurement is very close to the actual value. Precise measurements are very close, or nearly equal, to each other. Reliable measurements are both accurate and precise. An imprecise value may be a sign of an error in data collection. This kind of anomalous data may be excluded to avoid skewing the data and harming the investigation.

Other math skills include performing specific calculations, such as finding the mean, or average, value in a data set. The mean can be calculated by adding up all of the values in the data set and then dividing that sum by the number of values.

Hour	Number of Ducks Observed at a Pond
1	12
2	10
3	2
4	14
5	13
6	10
7	11

SEP Use Mathematics The data table shows how many ducks were seen at a pond every hour over the course of seven hours. Is there a data point that seems anomalous? If so, cross out that data point. Then, calculate the mean number of ducks on the pond. Round the mean to the nearest whole number.

Graphs

Graphs help scientists to interpret data by helping them to find trends or patterns in the data. A line graph displays data that show how one variable (the dependent or outcome variable) changes in response to another (the independent or test variable). The slope and shape of a graph line can reveal patterns and help scientists to make predictions. For example, line graphs can help you to spot patterns of change over time.

Scientists use bar graphs to compare data across categories or subjects that may not affect each other. The heights of the bars make it easy to compare those quantities. A circle graph, also known as a pie chart, shows the proportions of different parts of a whole.

Write About It
You and a friend record the distance you travel every 15 minutes on a one-hour bike trip. Your friend wants to display the data as a circle graph. Explain whether or not this is the best type of graph to display your data. If not, suggest another graph to use.

85

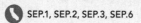

SEP.1, SEP.2, SEP.3, SEP.6

The Engineering Design Process

Engineers are builders and problem solvers. Chemical engineers experiment with new fuels made from algae. Civil engineers design roadways and bridges. Bioengineers develop medical devices and prosthetics. The common trait among engineers is an ability to identify problems and design solutions to solve them. Engineers use a creative process that relies on scientific methods to help guide them from a concept or idea all the way to the final product.

Define the Problem

To identify or define a problem, different questions need to be asked: *What are the effects of the problem? What are the likely causes? What other factors could be involved?* Sometimes the obvious, immediate cause of a problem may be the result of another problem that may not be immediately apparent. For example, climate change results in different weather patterns, which in turn can affect organisms that live in certain habitats. So engineers must be aware of all the possible effects of potential solutions. Engineers must also take into account how well different solutions deal with the different causes of the problem.

Reflect Write about a problem that you encountered in your life that had both immediate, obvious causes as well as less-obvious and less-immediate ones.

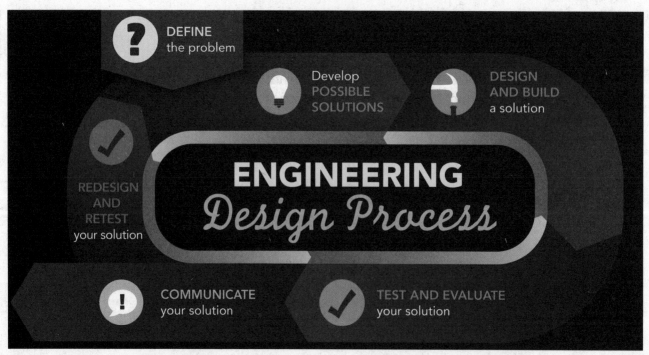

DEFINE the problem

Develop POSSIBLE SOLUTIONS

DESIGN AND BUILD a solution

REDESIGN AND RETEST your solution

ENGINEERING *Design Process*

COMMUNICATE your solution

TEST AND EVALUATE your solution

As engineers consider problems and design solutions, they must identify and categorize the criteria and constraints of the project.

Criteria are the factors that must be met or accomplished by the solution. For example, a gardener who wants to protect outdoor plants from deer and rabbits may say that the criteria for the solution are "plants are no longer eaten" and "plant growth is not inhibited in any way." The gardener then knows the plants cannot simply be sealed off from the environment, because the plants will not receive sunlight and water.

The same gardener will likely have constraints on his solution, such as budget for materials and time that is available for working on the project. By setting constraints, a solution can be designed that will be successful without introducing a new set of problems. No one wants to spend $500 on materials to protect $100 worth of tomatoes and cucumbers.

Develop Possible Solutions

After the problem has been identified, and the criteria and constraints identified, an engineer will consider possible solutions. This often involves working in teams with other engineers and designers to brainstorm ideas and research materials that can be used in the design.

It's important for engineers to think creatively and explore all potential solutions. If you wanted to design a bicycle that was safer and easier to ride than a traditional bicycle, then you would want more than just one or two solutions. Having multiple ideas to choose from increases the likelihood that you will develop a solution that meets the criteria and constraints. In addition, different ideas that result from brainstorming can often lead to new and better solutions to an existing problem.

Make Meaning

Using the example of a garden that is vulnerable to wild animals such as deer, make a list of likely constraints on an engineering solution to the problem you identified before. Determine if there are common traits among the constraints, and identify categories for them.

Design a Solution

Engineers then develop the idea that they feel best solves the problem. Once a solution has been chosen, engineers and designers get to work building a model or prototype of the solution. A model may involve sketching on paper or using computer software to construct a model of the solution. A prototype is a working model of the solution.

Building a model or prototype helps an engineer determine whether a solution meets the criteria and stays within the constraints. During this stage of the process, engineers must often deal with new problems and make any necessary adjustments to the model or prototype.

Test and Evaluate a Solution

Whether testing a model or a prototype, engineers use scientific processes to evaluate their solutions. Multiple experiments, tests, or trials are conducted, data are evaluated, and results and analyses are communicated. New criteria or constraints may emerge as a result of testing. In most cases, a solution will require some refinement or revision, even if it has been through successful testing. Refining a solution is necessary if there are new constraints, such as less money or available materials. Additional testing may be done to ensure that a solution satisfies local, state, or federal laws or standards.

Make Meaning Think about an aluminum beverage can. What would happen if the price or availability of aluminum changed so much that cans needed to be made of a new material? What would the criteria and constraints be on the development of a new can?

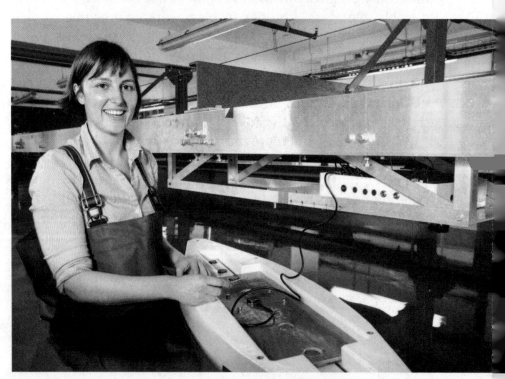

A naval architect sets up a model to test how the the hull's design responds to waves.

Communicate the Solution

Engineers need to communicate the final design to the people who will manufacture the product. This may include sketches, detailed drawings, computer simulations, and written text. Engineers often provide evidence that was collected during the testing stage. This evidence may include graphs and data tables that support the decisions made for the final design.

If there is feedback about the solution, then the engineers and designers must further refine the solution. This might involve making minor adjustments to the design, or it might mean bigger modifications to the design based on new criteria or constraints. Any changes in the design will require additional testing to make sure that the changes work as intended.

Redesign and Retest the Solution

At different steps in the engineering design process, a solution usually must be revised and retested. Many designs fail to work perfectly, even after models and prototypes are built, tested, and evaluated. Engineers must be ready to analyze new results and deal with any new problems that arise. Troubleshooting, or fixing design problems, allows engineers to adjust the design to improve on how well the solution meets the need.

SEP Design Solutions Suppose you are an engineer at an aerospace company. Your team is designing a rover to be used on a future NASA space mission. A family member doesn't understand why so much of your team's time is taken up with testing and retesting the rover design. What are three things you would tell your relative to explain why testing and retesting are so important to the engineering design process?

....

....

....

....

....

....

....

....

Safety Symbols

These symbols warn of possible dangers in the laboratory and remind you to work carefully.

 Safety Goggles Wear safety goggles to protect your eyes in any activity involving chemicals, flames or heating, or glassware.

 Lab Apron Wear a laboratory apron to protect your skin and clothing from damage.

 Breakage Handle breakable materials, such as glassware, with care. Do not touch broken glassware.

 Heat-Resistant Gloves Use an oven mitt or other hand protection when handling hot materials, such as hot plates or hot glassware.

 Plastic Gloves Wear disposable plastic gloves when working with harmful chemicals and organisms. Keep your hands away from your face, and dispose of the gloves according to your teacher's instructions.

 Heating Use a clamp or tongs to pick up hot glassware. Do not touch hot objects with your bare hands.

 Flames Before you work with flames, tie back loose hair and clothing. Follow your teacher's instructions about lighting and extinguishing flames.

 No Flames When using flammable materials, make sure there are no flames, sparks, or other exposed heat sources present.

 Corrosive Chemical Avoid getting acid or other corrosive chemicals on your skin or clothing or in your eyes. Do not inhale the vapors. Wash your hands after the activity.

 Poison Do not let any poisonous chemical come into contact with your skin, and do not inhale its vapors. Wash your hands when you are finished with the activity.

 Fumes Work in a well-ventilated area when harmful vapors may be involved. Avoid inhaling vapors directly. Test an odor only when directed to do so by your teacher, and use a wafting motion to direct the vapor toward your nose.

 Sharp Object Scissors, scalpels, knives, needles, pins, and tacks can cut your skin. Always direct a sharp edge or point away from yourself and others.

 Animal Safety Treat live or preserved animals or animal parts with care to avoid harming the animals or yourself. Wash your hands when you are finished with the activity.

 Plant Safety Handle plants only as directed by your teacher. If you are allergic to certain plants, tell your teacher; do not do an activity involving those plants. Avoid touching harmful plants such as poison ivy. Wash your hands when you are finished with the activity.

 Electric Shock To avoid electric shock, never use electrical equipment around water, when the equipment is wet, or when your hands are wet. Be sure cords are untangled and cannot trip anyone. Unplug equipment not in use.

 Physical Safety When an experiment involves physical activity, avoid injuring yourself or others. Alert your teacher if there is any reason you should not participate.

 Disposal Dispose of chemicals and other laboratory materials safely. Follow the instructions from your teacher.

 Hand Washing Wash your hands thoroughly when finished with an activity. Use soap and warm water. Rinse well.

 General Safety Awareness When this symbol appears, follow the instructions provided. When you are asked to develop your own procedure in a lab, have your teacher approve your plan.

Periodic Table of Elements

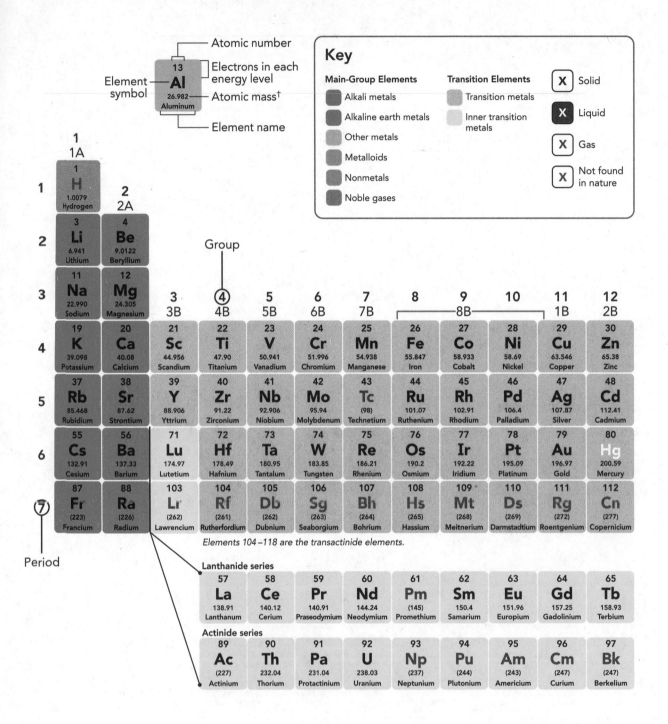

Elements 104–118 are the transactinide elements.

†The atomic masses in parentheses are the mass numbers of the longest-lived isotope of elements for which a standard atomic mass cannot be defined.

					18 8A
					2 **He** 4.0026 Helium
13 3A	14 4A	15 5A	16 6A	17 7A	
5 **B** 10.81 Boron	6 **C** 12.011 Carbon	7 **N** 14.007 Nitrogen	8 **O** 15.999 Oxygen	9 **F** 18.998 Fluorine	10 **Ne** 20.179 Neon
13 **Al** 26.982 Aluminum	14 **Si** 28.086 Silicon	15 **P** 30.974 Phosphorus	16 **S** 32.06 Sulfur	17 **Cl** 35.453 Chlorine	18 **Ar** 39.948 Argon
31 **Ga** 69.72 Gallium	32 **Ge** 72.59 Germanium	33 **As** 74.922 Arsenic	34 **Se** 78.96 Selenium	35 **Br** 79.904 Bromine	36 **Kr** 83.80 Krypton
49 **In** 114.82 Indium	50 **Sn** 118.69 Tin	51 **Sb** 121.75 Antimony	52 **Te** 127.60 Tellurium	53 **I** 126.90 Iodine	54 **Xe** 131.30 Xenon
81 **Tl** 204.37 Thallium	82 **Pb** 207.2 Lead	83 **Bi** 208.98 Bismuth	84 **Po** (209) Polonium	85 **At** (210) Astatine	86 **Rn** (222) Radon
113 **Nh** (284) Nihonium	114 **Fl** (289) Flerovium	115 **Mc** (288) Moscovium	116 **Lv** (292) Livermorium	117 **Ts** (294) Tennessine	118 **Og** (294) Oganesson

66 **Dy** 162.50 Dysprosium	67 **Ho** 164.93 Holmium	68 **Er** 167.26 Erbium	69 **Tm** 168.93 Thulium	70 **Yb** 173.04 Ytterbium
98 **Cf** (251) Californium	99 **Es** (252) Einsteinium	100 **Fm** (257) Fermium	101 **Md** (258) Mendelevium	102 **No** (259) Nobelium

GLOSSARY

A

abiotic factor A nonliving part of an organism's habitat.

alluvial fan A wide, sloping deposit of sediment formed where a stream leaves a mountain range.

atom The basic unit from which all matter is made.

autotroph An organism that is able to capture energy from sunlight or chemicals and use it to produce its own food.

B

biodiversity The number and variety of different species in an area.

biotic factor A living or once living part of an organism's habitat.

boiling point The temperature at which a liquid boils.

C

cellular respiration The process in which oxygen and glucose undergo a complex series of chemical reactions inside cells, releasing energy.

chemical change A change in which one or more substances combine or break apart to form new substances.

chemical property A characteristic of a substance that describes its ability to change into different substances.

chemical weathering The process that breaks down rock through chemical changes.

chlorophyll A green photosynthetic pigment found in the chloroplasts of plants, algae, and some bacteria.

closed system A system in which no matter is allowed to enter or leave.

commensalism A type of symbiosis between two species in which one species benefits and the other species is neither helped nor harmed.

community All the different populations that live together in a certain area.

competition The struggle between organisms to survive as they attempt to use the same limited resources in the same place at the same time.

compound A substance made of two or more elements chemically combined in a specific ratio, or proportion.

compression Stress that squeezes rock until it folds or breaks.

condensation The change in state from a gas to a liquid.

conservation The practice of using less of a resource so that it can last longer.

consumer An organism that obtains energy by feeding on other organisms.

continental glacier A glacier that covers much of a continent or large island.

convergent boundary A plate boundary where two plates move toward each other.

crust The layer of rock that forms Earth's outer surface.

crystal A solid in which the atoms are arranged in a pattern that repeats again and again.

crystallization The process by which atoms are arranged to form a material with a crystal structure.

crystallize To form a crystal structure.

D

decomposer An organism that gets energy by breaking down biotic wastes and dead organisms and returns raw materials to the soil and water.

deflation The process by which wind removes surface materials.

delta A landform made of sediment that is deposited where a river flows into an ocean or lake.

density The measurement of how much mass of a substance is contained in a given volume.

deposition Process in which sediment is laid down in new locations.

desalination A process that removes salt from sea water to make fresh water.

divergent boundary A plate boundary where two plates move away from each other.

dormant Term used to describe a volcano that is not currently acrtive but able to become active in the future.

drought A long period of low precipitation.

E

earthquake The shaking that results from the movement of rock beneath Earth's surface.

ecological restoration The practice of helping a degraded or destroyed ecosystem recover from damage.

ecology The study of how organisms interact with each other and their environment.

ecosystem The community of organisms that live in a particular area, along with their nonliving environment.

ecosystem services The benefits that humans derive from ecosystems.

element A pure substance that cannot be broken down into other substances by chemical or physical means.

energy pyramid A diagram that shows the amount of energy that moves from one feeding level to another in a food web.

erosion The process by which water, ice, wind, or gravity moves weathered particles of rock and soil.

evaporation The process by which molecules at the surface of a liquid absorb enough energy to change to a gas.

extinct volcano Term used to describe a volcano that is no longer active and unlikely to erupt again

extinction The disappearance of all members of a species from Earth.

F

fault A break in Earth's crust along which rocks move.

fermentation The process by which cells release energy by breaking down food molecules without using oxygen.

flood An overflowing of water in a normally dry area.

flood plain The flat, wide area of land along a river.

food chain A series of events in an ecosystem in which organisms transfer energy by eating and by being eaten.

food web The pattern of overlapping feeding relationships or food chains among the various organisms in an ecosystem.

fossil fuel Energy-rich substance formed from the remains of organisms.

freezing point The temperature at which a liquid freezes.

G

gas A state of matter with no definite shape or volume.

glacier Any large mass of ice that moves slowly over land.

groundwater Water that fills the cracks and spaces in underground soil and rock layers.

H

habitat An environment that provides the things a specific organism needs to live, grow, and reproduce.

heterotroph An organism that cannot make its own food and gets food by consuming other living things.

hot spot An area where magma from deep within the mantle melts through the crust above it.

humus Dark-colored organic material in soil.

hurricane A tropical storm that has winds of about 119 kilometers per hour or higher.

I

ice age Time in Earth's history during which glaciers covered large parts of the surface.

igneous rock A type of rock that forms from the cooling of molten rock at or below the surface.

inner core A dense sphere of solid iron and nickel at the center of Earth.

invasive species Species that are not native to a habitat and can out-compete native species in an ecosystem.

K

keystone species A species that influences the survival of many other species in an ecosystem.

GLOSSARY

L

lava Liquid magma that reaches the surface.

limiting factor An environmental factor that causes a population to decrease in size.

liquid A state of matter that has no definite shape but has a definite volume.

loess A wind-formed deposit made of fine particles of clay and silt.

longshore drift The movement of water and sediment down a beach caused by waves coming in to shore at an angle.

M

magma A molten mixture of rock-forming substances, gases, and water from the mantle.

magnitude The measurement of an earthquake's strength based on seismic waves and movement along faults.

mantle The layer of hot, solid material between Earth's crust and core.

mass A measure of how much matter is in an object.

mass movement Any one of several processes by which gravity moves sediment downhill.

matter Anything that has mass and takes up space.

mechanical weathering The type of weathering in which rock is physically broken into smaller pieces.

melting point The temperature at which a substance changes from a solid to a liquid; the same as the freezing point, or temperature at which a liquid changes to a solid.

metamorphic rock A type of rock that forms from an existing rock that is changed by heat, pressure, or chemical reactions.

mid-ocean ridge An undersea mountain chain where new ocean floor is produced; a divergent plate boundary under the ocean.

mineral A naturally occurring solid that can form by inorganic processes and that has a crystal structure and a definite chemical composition.

mixture Two or more substances that are together in the same place, but their atoms are not chemically bonded.

molecule A group of two or more atoms held together by chemical bonds.

mutualism A type of symbiosis in which both species benefit from living together.

N

natural resource Anything naturally occurring in the environment that humans use.

nonrenewable resource A natural resource that is not replaced in a useful time frame.

nuclear fission The splitting of an atom's nucleus into two nuclei, which releases a great deal of energy.

O

ocean trench An undersea valley that represents one of the deepest parts of the ocean.

open system A system in which matter can enter from or escape to the surroundings.

ore A mineral deposit large enough and valuable enough for it to be extracted from the ground.

organism A living thing.

outer core A layer of molten iron and nickel that surrounds the inner core of Earth.

P

parasitism A type of symbiosis in which one organism lives with, on, or in a host and harms it.

petroleum Liquid fossil fuel; oil.

photosynthesis The process by which plants and other autotrophs capture and use light energy to make food from carbon dioxide and water.

physical change A change that alters the form or appearance of a material but does not make the material into another substance.

physical property A characteristic of a pure substance that can be observed without changing it into another substance.

pioneer species The first species to populate an area during succession.

plucking The process by which a glacier picks up rocks as it flows over the land.

polymer A long chain of molecules made up of repeating units.

population All the members of one species living in the same area.

precipitation Any form of water that falls from clouds and reaches Earth's surface as rain, snow, sleet, or hail.

predation An interaction in which one organism kills another for food or nutrients.

producer An organism that can make its own food.

product A substance formed as a result of a chemical reaction.

R

reactant A substance that enters into a chemical reaction.

rock cycle A series of processes on the surface and inside Earth that slowly changes rocks from one kind to another.

runoff Water that flows over the ground surface rather than soaking into the ground.

S

sand dune A deposit of wind-blown sand.

sea-floor spreading The process by which molten material adds new oceanic crust to the ocean floor.

sediment Small, solid pieces of material that come from rocks or the remains of organisms; earth materials deposited by erosion.

sedimentary rock A type of rock that forms when particles from other rocks or the remains of plants and animals are pressed and cemented together.

seismic wave Vibrations that travel through Earth carrying the energy released during an earthquake.

shearing Stress that pushes masses of rock in opposite directions, in a sideways movement.

soil The loose, weathered material on Earth's surface in which plants can grow.

solid A state of matter that has a definite shape and a definite volume.

solubility A measure of how much a substance dissolves in another substance.

storm A violent disturbance in the atmosphere.

storm surge A "dome" of water that sweeps across the coast where a hurricane lands.

stream A channel through which water is continually flowing downhill.

stress A force that acts on rock to change its shape or volume.

subduction The process by which oceanic crust sinks beneath a deep-ocean trench and back into the mantle at a convergent plate boundary.

sublimation The change in state from a solid directly to a gas without passing through the liquid state.

substance A single kind of matter that is pure and has a specific set of properties.

succession The series of predictable changes that occur in a community over time.

sustainability The ability of an ecosystem to maintain bioviersity and production indefinitely.

symbiosis Any relationship in which two species live closely together and that benefits at least one of the species.

synthetic Created or manufactured by humans; not found occurring in nature

T

temperature How hot or cold something is; a measure of the average energy of motion of the particles of a substance; the measure of the average kinetic energy of the particles of a substance.

tension Stress that stretches rock so that it becomes thinner in the middle.

thermal energy The total kinetic and potential energy of all the particles of an object.

thunderstorm A small storm often accompanied by heavy precipitation and frequent thunder and lightning.

till The sediments deposited directly by a glacier.

tornado A rapidly whirling, funnel-shaped cloud that reaches down to touch Earth's surface.

GLOSSARY

transform boundary A plate boundary where two plates move past each other in opposite directions.

tributary A stream or river that flows into a larger river.

tsunami A giant wave usually caused by an earthquake beneath the ocean floor.

U

uniformitarianism The geologic principle that the same geologic processes that operate today operated in the past to change Earth's surface.

V

valley glacier A long, narrow glacier that forms when snow and ice build up in a mountain valley.

vaporization The change of state from a liquid to a gas.

volcano A weak spot in the crust where magma has come to the surface.

volume The amount of space that matter occupies.

W

weight A measure of the force of gravity acting on an object.

INDEX

Page number in **Bold** are vocabulary terms. *Italic* page numbers are of charts, graphs, pictures, and features.

CREDITS

Photography

Photo locators denoted as follows: Top (T), Center (C), Bottom (B), Left (L), Right (R), Background (Bkgd)

Covers

Front: Casey Kiernan/Moment/Getty Images; Meganopierson/Shutterstock; Zoonar GmbH/Alamy Stock Photo; Stocktrek Images, Inc./Alamy Stock Photo; Back: Marinello/DigitalVision Vectors/Getty Images

Instructional Segment 1

iv: Nick Lundgren/Shutterstock; vi: Joe McBride/Getty Images; vi: George Ostertag/AGE Fotostock; vii: Makieni/Fotolia; viiiT: Fabriziobalconi/Fotolia; viii: Bkgd Brian J. Skerry/National Geographic/Getty Images; ixB: Dale Kolke/ZUMA Press/Newscom; x: Zoonar/Jamie Pham/AGE Fotostock 003BL: Randimal/Shutterstock; 003BR: All Canada Photos/Alamy Stock Photo; 004: Jamie Pham/Alamy Stock Photo; 008: George Ostertag/AGE Fotostock; 012: Sami Sarkis RM CC/Alamy Stock Photo; 014Bkgd: Lazyllama/Shutterstock; 014BL: Subinpumsom/Fotolia; 015BL: Borroko72/Fotolia; 015BR: Arpad Nagy-Bagoly/Fotolia; 016BR: Anyka/123RF; 016C: James Steidl/Shutterstock; 018TC: Smereka/Shutterstock; 018TR: GIPhotoStock/Science Source; 019TCR: Bert Folsom/123RF; 019TR: Lepas2004/iStock/Getty Images; 021BC: SuperStock; 021Bkgd: Massimo Pizzotti/AGE Fotostock/Superstock; 021TR: David L. Ryan/The Boston Globe/Getty Images; 022: Michelle McMahon/Moment/Getty Images; 024T: Martin Shields/Alamy Stock Photo; 024TR: Martin Shields/Alamy Stock Photo; 025BR: Hal Beral/VWPics/AP Images; 025CR: GIPhotoStock/Science Source; 025L: Hitandrun IKON Images/Newscom; 026: Brigitte Merz/LOOK Die Bildagentur der Fotografen GmbH/Alamy Stock Photo; 028CR: RF Company/Alamy Stock Photo; 028T: Victor21041958/Fotolia; 028L: Denis Radovanovic/Shutterstock; 028R: Siim Sepp/Alamy Stock Photo; 030: Kraig Lieb/Alamy Stock Photo; 032: Sergey Dobrydnev/Shutterstock; 033BL: Stephanie Frey/Fotolia; 033BR: Kzen/Shutterstock; 033BCL: Vinicef/Alamy Stock Photo; 033BCR: Vinicef/Alamy Stock Photo; 034TL: Studio on line/Shutterstock; 034TR: 123RF; 034CL: Fuse/Corbis/Getty Images; 034CR: Charles D. Winters/Science Source; 036Bkgd: Peter Barritt/Alamy Stock Photo; 036BL: Paul Souders/Alamy Stock Photo; 037: Arndt Sven-Erik/Arterra Picture Library/Alamy Stock Photo; 039: Kiyoshi Takahase Segundo/Alamy Stock Photo; 042: Torontonian/Alamy Stock Photo; 043: USantos/Fotolia; 046: Makieni/Fotolia; 048: Unlisted Images, Inc./Alamy Stock Photo; 050: Dmytro Skorobogatov/Alamy Stock Photo; 051T: Erika8213/Fotolia; 051BL: Marco Cavina/Shutterstock; 051BR: CrackerClips Stock Media/Shutterstock; 052BCL: Robyn Mackenzie/Shutterstock; 052BL: Fototrips/Fotolia; 053BL: Kropic/Fotolia; 053BR: Rony Zmiri/Fotolia; 054BL: Wiklander/Shutterstock; 054BR: Oriori/Fotolia; 057BCR: Özgür Güvenç/Fotolia; 057CR: Xiaoliangge/Fotolia; 058: WavebreakMediaMicro/Fotolia; 059: Dennis Frates/Alamy Stock Photo; 062TC: PhotoAlto/Odilon Dimier/Getty Images; 062TL: Petr Malyshev/Fotolia; 062TR: Uygaar/Getty Images; 064CR: Cultura Creative (RF)/Alamy Stock Photo; 065: Charles D. Winters/Science Source; 068B: Kylewolfe/RooM/Getty Images; 068BC: Pakhnyushcha/Shutterstock; 068C: Reika/Shutterstock; 068CR: Richard Megna/Fundamental Photographs; 072: Mrallen/Fotolia; 073: Bestphotostudio/Fotolia; 076BL: Turtle Rock Scientific/Science Source; 076BR: Sciencephotos/Alamy Stock Photo.